FASHION MATH™
MAKE-OVER

THE LANE BRYANT

FASHION MATH™

MAKE-OVER

The Complete Fashion Guide
For Women Size 14 and Up

Printed especially for LANE BRYANT by
the Special Sales Department of
Dell Publishing
a division of
The Bantam Doubleday Dell Publishing Group, Inc.
1 Dag Hammarskjold Plaza
New York, New York 10017

ISBN: 0-440-14597-X

Printed in the United States of America

October 1987

10 9 8 7 6 5 4 3 2 1

Writer: Kalia Lulow

Co-writer: Wanda Geddie

Designer: Doug Turshen

Illustrator: Steve Butow

Photographer: Gil Gilbert

Book Packager: Madeleine Morel, 2M Communication Ltd.

This book is

dedicated to every Lane Bryant
customer... past, present and future...
and to the American women size 14 and up
who have been neglected by
the fashion world for far too long!
Your time is now!

Acknowledgments

Our sincere thanks to the many people whose time and assistance were invaluable in making this book possible.

To Eleanor Grober for developing the plan for the book, researching and contributing significantly to it, and coordinating the project. An especially heartfelt thank you to Koko Hashim, Lane Bryant Director of Fashion Coordination. Her incredible knowledge of everything to do with fashion, her imagination, diligence and organization were beyond value in the preparation and execution of this book. To Marilyn Kahn for making the very intricate subject of foundation garments understandable to the authors. And to the following for their expert advice, suggestions and cooperation: Joanne Del Dotto, Ann Early, Mary Ann Molinari and Diane Tarbell.

To Joan Moran of Dell Publishing for her enthusiasm and cooperation in shepherding this book from the idea stage to the finished product. To Steve Butow for his delightful illustrations. To Doug Turshen for his excellent book design. And to Madeleine Morel for packaging the project.

Finally, to Kalia Lulow for the wonderful sense of joy, excitement and discovery she conveys in the telling of the Lane Bryant Fashion Math™ story. And to Wanda Gayle Geddie for showing us how to turn a full figure into a fashion asset, proving once and for all that beauty comes in all sizes... and looks especially gorgeous in sizes 14 and up!

Table of Contents

How to Use the Lane Bryant Fashion Math™ Make-Over 8

The Fashion Math™ Formula 9
Fashion Math™ Total System 9

Your Glorious Style 10

The Expression of the Real You 12
Developing Glorious Style 12
Your Style Checklist 14
Style in Action 14

New Fashion Options 16

Working with Color 19
Color Choices 22
Fabrics 26
Wearing Stripes 28
Checks and Plaids 29
Bold Prints 30
Small and Medium Prints 31
Fashion Directions 32
Silhouette News 34
Fashion Personality 37

Shape and Style 37

Triangle 44
Rectangle 46
Diamond 48
Circle 50
Hourglass 52
"V" 54

Fashion Choices, Fashion Basics *42*

Dresses *58*

Sweaters *60*

Blouses *62*

Shirts *64*

Jackets *66*

Skirts *68*

Pants *70*

T-shirts and Shorts *72*

Fleece *74*

Swimwear *76*

Coats and Outerwear *78*

Accessories *80*

Jewelry *81*

Belts *84*

Scarves *86*

Bows, Berets, and Hats *87*

Shoes and Hosiery *88*

Intimate Apparel *90*

The Polishing Touch *94*

Makeup *96*

Hair *98*

Fashion Math™ Make-Overs *100*

Fashion Math™ Wardrobe Building *101*

Fashion Math™ Make-Overs *106*

Shopping *124*

Lane Bryant's Shopping System *125*

Parting Words from Wanda *128*

How to Use the Lane Bryant Fashion Math™ Make-Over

Lane Bryant believes that plus-sized fashion adds up to a wonderful world of beautiful clothes and exciting styles. And Fashion Math™ is the step-by-step formula that can help you build the versatile, attractive, affordable wardrobe of your dreams, while helping you achieve your own glorious style.

To help you become your most attractive self, we start with building your inner self-confidence—setting aside the old myths that have made it difficult for plus-sized women to explore the Fashion Options available to them. Gone are the old do's and don'ts that have made women over a size 14 feel that many choices in styles, colors and fabrics were off limits to them. Today the possibilities are endless—and exciting!

Then we look at each part of the fashion equation to show you how you can create a total wardrobe. Never again will you become frustrated going from store to store trying to find clothing that fits *and* boasts the latest style. Lane Bryant has created collections that are suited to all your fashion dreams and needs.

Chapter by chapter, we will examine the new Fashion Options that are available and show you how they work together. The end result is that you can create many outfits for work, play or evenings without ending up with a closet full of "nothing to wear."

The Fashion Math™ formula

All the clothing illustrated in this book is divided into Fashion Choices and Fashion Basics. In Chapter Six, Choices and Basics are used to create mix-and-match wardrobes. We will demonstrate that with as few as seven items of clothing, you can create more than a dozen outfits. You'll see how you can fill your closet with beautiful versatile clothing without emptying your pocketbook.

The total make-over

Fashion Math™ helps you create a whole new look. From head to toe, we will explore how you can emphasize your assets. Makeup and hairstyles, shoes and hosiery, foundations and accessories—nothing is overlooked.

The results

After you have read this book, you will become more self-confident, armed with the information you need to shop for the clothing that will be the most flattering and comfortable.

Lane Bryant's special program

Lane Bryant can help you put your new knowledge into practice. We have designed a special program that focuses on the total Fashion Math™ concept. All clothes in every season's collections are dyed to match. The printed shirt you love is guaranteed to look great with the skirt that flatters your figure. The exciting Venezia™ fleece top will complement the pants you choose.

Our sales staff is specially trained to help you put together your Fashion Math™ Make-Over wardrobe. You can rely on them for sound advice and judgment.

Fashion Math's™ total system

Step One: Take the time to explore your inner style. Use Chapter One, *Your Glorious Style*, to free your imagination and develop self-confidence.

Step Two: Explore the Fashion Options that are available to you. Use Chapter Two, *New Fashion Options*, to learn about the choices you have in colors, prints and patterns. Discover the magic of using different silhouettes to complement your figure.

Step Three: Learn to assess your figure using Chapter Three, *Shape and Style*. Each body shape has distinct fashion advantages. Learning how to choose clothes that emphasize your strengths is an important part of assembling a wardrobe.

Step Four: Become familiar with *Fashion Choices and Fashion Basics*. In Chapter Four, we survey the various styles of dresses, sweaters, shirts, blouses, jackets, skirts, pants, shorts, swimwear, coats and accessories. This tour offers a concise look at the important fashion elements that comprise a complete wardrobe.

Step Five: Chapter Five, *The Polishing Touch*, gives you a compact, easy-to-follow lesson on using makeup and hairstyling to accent your best features.

Step Six: Don't overlook Chapter Six, *Fashion Math™ Make-Over*, the exciting wrap-up that brings together the various elements that will allow you to achieve your new fashion look. You will meet four spirited women who will show you how the make-over transformed them. And you will see just how simple it is to bring out the best in yourself.

Step Seven: Chapter Seven, *Shopping*, gets you ready to go out and take the stores by storm! When you are comfortable and confident with your style *and* certain that you will find the clothes you want, shopping is a pleasure. So let's not wait to get started. Turn to Chapter One, *Your Glorious Style*, and you're on the road to discovering how terrific you can look.

Your Glorious Style

11

Your Style is the Expression of the Real You!

Lane Bryant knows that you are ready to break out of the fashion doldrums. The world is moving toward a sense of style that is bigger, fuller-figured, more womanly. From a health standpoint, the dangers of overdieting have been well-established. However, many larger-sized women have not had a chance to cultivate their own sense of style because of our long-standing obsession with being thin.

Those days are gone forever.

Forget every piece of advice you've ever heard about what the plus-sized woman can and cannot wear. Every woman deserves clothes that are beautiful. We at Lane Bryant have revolutionized the plus-sized fashion world. Now there is a great variety of shirts, skirts, sweaters, pants—literally anything you might want to complement your lifestyle, personality and appearance. You are about to enter a wonderland of choices. Lane Bryant has designed plus-sized fashions that will make it easy to express your own unique style . . . and proudly create a wardrobe that presents your most attractive self to the world!

Lane Bryant has developed these incredible changes in plus-sized fashion over the past several years. First we tackled the sizing problems in the plus-sized world. We established rational, consistent and accurate larger sizes, with cuts and fits that reflect the needs of our customers. Now we have a complete line of clothing in sizes 14 to 28 for fun, for fancy and for work, not only reflecting the best designs and the most exciting fashions, but providing good quality at good prices. Now you can shop for the clothes of your dreams—and have your dreams come true.

Developing glorious style: Style isn't something you buy in a jar and spread over yourself. Style comes from within. Everyone has a personal style; you may simply need to coax yours out of hiding.

Frankly, the plus-sized woman has often suffered from low self-esteem, and lack of confidence makes it hard to develop style. Now that the world is acknowledging that beauty comes in all shapes and sizes, you can shed all restraints. This book will act as your guide, helping you to establish your own style.

Wanda Gayle Geddie
5'8" 27 years old
Size 14
Home: Originally, Jackson, Mississippi; now, Brooklyn, New York.

> **There's no reason why a big girl like me can't feel and look beautiful. We all want to be healthy, but some of us are just not made to be thin. I believe true style has to reflect your inner nature...it can't be forced...**

> **When I choose clothing, I ask myself, 'What do I want to say about myself?' I want clothes that work for me. I must be comfortable in them."** —Wanda

Your style checklist

Style is different from fashion. Fashions constantly change. From one season to the next, hems go up or down, shoulders are padded or unpadded. Style, on the other hand, is consistent. It is the foundation upon which you build a fashion look. To use fashion effectively, you must first identify your individual style. Once you've done that, you are ready to indulge every fashion dream you've ever had!

Open up your imagination

To get acquainted with your own sense of style, set aside all practical considerations. Don't worry about what you've heard you *should* think. Just close your eyes and dream for a moment.

● What outfit have you seen in a magazine or a store recently that made you say, "I'd love to wear that, but I'll never be able to"? Chances are it is just your style.

● Do you have a favorite color that you have never worn? Listen to your inner voice. That's probably the right color for your next outfit.

● What is your dream dress for a fancy party? Sleek sequins or cascading ruffles? With the right cut and fit it is more than possible—it is perfect.

Your inner voice will tell you the right direction to go in. Let it out. Express your own unique style.

Style in action

A pleasing style is not stiff and motionless. Style is motion, a presentation of yourself in action. The way a woman walks across a room has more to do with the impression she creates than any other quality. Posture and poise are incredibly important. How you walk, sit and place your legs and hands paints a portrait of you that can be arrestingly beautiful. Your body language affects how you look more than the tilt of your nose, the color of your eyes or the weight of your body.

Answer the following questions with what you <u>feel</u>, not what you <u>do</u>:

1. I like clothes that are:
a) tailored
b) layered
c) blousey or full

2. I think of myself as:
a) sporty
b) formal
c) dramatic
d) conservative
e) very feminine
f) versatile

3. I wish I appeared more:
a) businesslike
b) casual
c) romantic

There are no right or wrong answers. You may feel that you're a combination of qualities. You may have an image of yourself that isn't included in these lists. That's good. What you want to do is become aware of your own personal flair. Think about how you answered these questions, and remember your reactions. Next time you look through a fashion magazine or go to a store, evaluate what you see. Ask yourself, "Is that dress my style? Is it a style I would like to have? If not, why not?"

You should select your clothes because they are what you *want*, not because you are reluctant to try something that may seem too bold.

How to improve your posture

- Stand with your lower back and shoulders against a wall. Are the outer ends of your shoulders drooping forward? Stretch out the top of your torso. Extend your shoulders backward.
- Feel your neck. Bring your head and chin up slightly and place your head flat against the wall. Your eyes should gaze straight ahead.
- Feel your shoulders. Are they tight? Raised up? Relax them downward. Keep them back. While you do this, breathe evenly.
- Standing with your back and head aligned, shoulders back but relaxed, turn your attention to your legs. Flex your knees, then stand with your weight distributed evenly between them.
- Put your hands on your hips.
- Tuck your pelvis under and tighten your tummy. Your fanny should be slightly tucked and the small of your back should be elongated.
- Point your toes directly forward.

Posture is particularly important for large-breasted women. They often feel pulled forward, or slump forward self-consciously. This only calls attention to a large bosom; the solution is better-fitting foundation garments (see Chapter Four). Once you have the proper support, good posture is simply a matter of discipline and attention.

Walking with pride will make you feel more attractive almost instantly. And feeling more attractive will inspire better posture. So remember, walk across a room with your head up, posture straight. Don't look like you are rushing to get out of view.

Adding fashion to style

Fashion is built upon style. This is where the fun begins, because fashion presents choices that can reflect your every mood, or create whatever image you want.

The basic element of fashion is surprise. Go for the unexpected. When you are assembling a fashion wardrobe, consider the possibilities of combining different fabrics, for example. Leather and denim may seem to be opposites, but together they create a sporty look. Although tweed and silk may seem as if they don't go together, the play of a smooth, well-draped silk blouse against a tweed jacket brings out the beauty of both. Likewise, you may have a very trim knit dress that always seemed "quiet," calling for simple pearls or dainty accessories. Try a wide red belt, a striped woven shawl or a big jeweled pin as an accent. *You* are making a fashion statement.

Establishing a style

Once you have a feel for your own unique style, it is time to put it into practice. (Chapter Six will show you how to shop for a wardrobe that is completely coordinated.) Shopping for style takes time. You can't put together a harmonious wardrobe from random purchases. You have to build it.

Being careful about your purchases doesn't mean you have to be timid, however. When you begin, make a bargain with yourself that you'll buy one item that is in a color, cut or fabric you've never worn before.

Besides the clothes you wear, style is achieved through:

- *Impeccable grooming.* Shining hair, a flashing smile, well-kept nails, fresh skin and well-pressed clothes are basics.
- *Naturalness.* Don't *adopt* a style, *develop* it. Never wear anything that feels like a costume. You want to be your most attractive self—not an imitation of someone else.
- *Enjoyment.* Getting dressed should delight you. It should make you smile. When others see you, they should smile, too. So let yourself dress with a touch of pizzazz— a splash of color, an unusual piece of jewelry. Remember, you can be eye-catching and be yourself.

Fashion tips

- **Use accessories to make bold fashion statements. Even if you aren't comfortable with a completely bold look, you can extend your style by adding daring accessories.**
- **When buying fashion items, start with one versatile piece, such as a sweater or jacket, that can be combined with many different outfits. Let yourself get used to new fashions.**
- **Don't hesitate to experiment in the stores with various pieces of clothing. Just checking out how you look and feel in different outfits will awaken your sense of style.**

New Fashion Options

It's a Whole New World of Plus-Sized Fashion Options

Color, pattern, fabric and *silhouette* are the four Fashion Options that you can explore to create your new personal style. Vivid colors, bold stripes, textured cables, sleek knits—there are no taboos. Size has nothing to do with the choices that are available to you. A woman can wear any color, pattern or fabric she chooses as long as it is in proportion to her body and suited to her Fashion Personality (a detailed discussion of Fashion Personalities starts on page 37).

Working with color

The fashion palette, like the painter's, must be used artfully. Whatever the overriding fashion trend is, the basic choices remain the same: colors and neutrals.

With so many choices, your best bet is to follow your instincts. Choose what makes you feel good. Color can be used to reflect your mood—and it can change it. You can beat the blues with a bright color or a calming combination of neutrals. Make color work for you and you'll soon be enjoying it as never before.

The color glossary

All colors are made from three primary colors: red, yellow and blue. *Brights* include colors such as true clear green, red, blue, yellow, purple, fuchsia, hot pink and orange. These bright colors may also be modified into darker or lighter variations, more complex shades such as deep jungle green, brilliant jewel tones or intense sun colors.

Mid-tones include coral, sky blue, daisy yellow, watermelon, jade and royal blue. *Pales*—the lightest gradations of color—come in the favorites: shades of peach, butter, lavender and soft pink that

19

range from gentle washes of tone to deeper and richer hues.

Neutrals are shades that can be worn as background colors because they work with both brights and pales. Pure black and white are considered neutrals, as are colors such as khaki and olive green. There are many families of neutrals:
- *Grey neutrals* include the range from silver to charcoal.
- *Grey-brown neutrals* include stone, taupe, mocha and bark.
- *Golden-brown neutrals* include ginger, ecru, camel and tobacco.
- *Red-brown neutrals* include clay, brick, redwood and mahogany.
- *Blue neutrals* include navy, indigo, chambray and slate.
- *Green neutrals* include sage, khaki, olive and forest.

"Fashion is fun. It's a chance to say, 'Watch out, world!' Larger-sized women actually have a fashion advantage because people respond so positively to seeing us look really great. They can tell we are happy about it, and that gives everyone a good feeling."—Wanda

Putting it all together

Combining colors is the trick that every fashion-conscious woman wants to master. Colors are either *warm* (yellow-based) or *cool* (blue-based). Basically, colors that are in the same family—either all warms or all cools—make the safest combinations. For example, warm orange and pink are sure to blend, as are bright blue and green. But warms and cools can be combined as well. The rule of thumb in this case is to let one color predominate. For example, if you blend red and blue (a strong red and an aqua blue), choose one to create the main impression. Let the other act as an accent.

Fabric choices

Fabrics in all their variations are the basis of your fashion wardrobe. Not only do fabrics make the fashion, they often make the difference between clothes that you love to wear and clothes that hang, neglected, in your closet. Combining different types of fabric in exciting, complementary ways is one of the keys to putting together a fashion wardrobe.

Working with patterns

Bold stripes, big geometric patterns or colorful all-over prints offer every woman an opportunity for self-expression, fun, sophistication and style. At Lane Bryant, we have designed special patterns that work with the plus-sized figure. They are all in proportion to the cut of the clothing and are designed to complement any figure. You may have to go simply on faith the first time you try on a garment with a big geometric pattern or a wide stripe, but don't hesitate to experiment at the store. With the help of our trained salespeople, you'll find that you are delighted by the impression you create when your wardrobe consists of a diverse range of patterns.

Stripes

Stripes can be narrow or bold, horizontal or vertical. They can come in one color plus white or in several colors—either contrasting or blending. They are suited to every lifestyle and personality and should be a basic in your mix-and-match wardrobe. Stripes are particularly useful in sweaters and tops where they add an element of interest against a plain skirt or pant. When you wear striped skirts or pants, vertical stripes or pinstripes are the most flattering.

Checks and plaids

Checks and plaids offer an enormous selection. The deep-toned plaids present a conservative yet colorful image, while a large check can be either dramatic or casual.

Checks include houndstooth, argyle, buffalo, gingham, grids and double grids. Plaids run the gamut from tartans to glen plaids. You can even mix and match checks and plaids if they are color-coordinated, but it takes a deft hand to learn how to make the look blend. You want to look exciting, not overly busy. The key: Keep one pattern very subtle and keep the colors in the same color family.

Prints

Prints are a limitless wardrobe resource. They are personal; they reflect your particular taste and style. It's important to experiment so that you can take advantage of fashion's prolific and diverse offering.

• *Big, bold prints* can be centered or dramatically asymmetrical. They are meant to be fun and are often found on fleece sweatshirts, T-shirts and sweater dresses. These big prints are high-spirited and meant to make you feel carefree and daring.

• *Medium and small prints* usually appear all over a fabric; they also can be effective as borders. Feminine prints include florals, scrolls, hearts and other delicate images. Medium and small prints work for all dresses, pants, skirts and tops. They are very flattering as accents on scarves.

• *Geometric prints* have straight-edged lines and shapes.

The silhouette

There are three current fashion silhouettes: fit-and-flare, long-over-lean and long-over-flare. For example, you may have a long outer jacket or sweater that is trim and extends to mid-thigh. If you combine it with a full skirt, you create a long-over-flare silhouette. The same sweater added to a trim knit skirt will create a long-over-lean line. By learning to vary the silhouettes you wear, you can add an extra element to your style.

Your Fashion Personality

The world of new Fashion Options comes together when you express your personality through color, pattern, fabric and silhouette. You aren't locked into one way of self-presentation, but you do have a basic Fashion Personality that influences your choices and gives you an overall style. Developing your Fashion Personality gives you the freedom and sense of fun you need to use fashion to advantage—to create the impression you want.

Let's look at each of these elements in more detail and see what your fashion future holds.

" Combining colors ... it's your chance to expand the number of outfits you own. I love to make a favorite skirt seem brand new by wearing it with different colored sweaters, blouses and accessories."
—Wanda

Silhouette tips

• **Use a silhouette in a way that flatters your figure. A silhouette should not end at a body point that you want to minimize. For example, a thick waist is accentuated by fit-and-flare, but is minimized by long-over-flare. You can make wide hips seem smaller if you balance them with shoulder padding and choose a long top that extends to mid-thigh, directing the eye below the widest point of your figure.**

• **Since proportion is the key to any silhouette, you want to create balance. If you have a figure that is heavier on the bottom than on top, you can put together a long-over-lean silhouette ... just add shoulder pads to create balance.**

• **To balance a figure that is full on top and thinner on the bottom, use soft, full skirts with trim, long jackets or shirts.**

• **To create the appearance of fit-and-flare, belt a long sweater or shirt with a wide leather belt or a thin belt that goes around the waist or hips. Keep shoulders strong and skirts full.**

• **A short silhouette doesn't mean a 16-inch miniskirt, simply a knee-length skirt with a leggy look. The shorter silhouette provides a great opportunity to experiment with new proportions.**

See page 34 for more silhouette news.

Color Choices

Painting your wardrobe with colors and neutrals is the first step in creating a fashion style.

There are two basic formulas that help you use color to assemble outfits that make a fashion statement.

Formula one: Head-to-toe

All brights, all pales or all neutrals combined in one ensemble create a monochromatic effect.

The four ensembles on page 23 use one color head-to-toe. This formula allows you to mix and match many different garments from your wardrobe, building a wide variety of outfits. Lane Bryant makes this easy to do, by creating a specific color palette every season and color-matching all separates so that you can combine your purchases effortlessly.

Tips

• Use jewelry and other accessories as accents by selecting items that are either in the lightest or darkest range of the all-over color. Notice the light ivory bracelet with the ecru and mocha skirt and sweater in the illustration.

• Use various gradations of your basic color to maintain the unified head-to-toe look but add rhythm and interest. The outfit in olive, pale khaki and khaki is harmonious, but also uses a variety of shades.

1. Brights
A vivid fuchsia jacket and skirt, combined with a fuchsia sweater that is accented with emerald green stripes, create a strong but unified impression.

2. Neutrals
The ecru-patterned full skirt and matching ecru "T" with a deep neck and a fitted bodice are in the same color family as the mocha cable-knit sweater and mocha-toned belt. Far right, the head-to-toe combination blends all-over neutrals from deep olive to pale khaki.

3. Pales
The plush peach corduroy pants and patterned peach sweater are set off by a daring splash of vivid yellow (shoes). Pale colors from head to toe provide a great backdrop for an unexpected flash of accent color.

1.   2.   3.   2.

Formula two: Colors in combination

Contrasting colors lets you expand the mix-and-match potential of your wardrobe. There are four basic ways to combine colors.

• *Accessory Accents.* Against a bright basic outfit, neutral-toned accessories give a gentle, pulled-together look. Vivid accents on pales and neutrals make a distinctive fashion look.

• *The Under-Accent.* Use an under-accent to bring color to a basically neutral three-piece outfit by wearing a pale or bright color under a jacket. Want to tone down a bright combination? Use a neutral under-accent to subdue the whole effect.

• *The Over-Accent.* An over-accent is a jacket, sweater or oversized shirt that is worn over a basic outfit, bringing accent color into a central position in your fashion formula. Against a pale or neutral background, an over-accent introduces a strong color that can make the simplest style look fresh.

• *The Half Split.* This combination lets you bring two or three colors together in a unified look. Using a neutral as the basic building block for an outfit, you can add two other colors—say, two cool pales such as pistachio and sky blue. If you begin with a bright as your basic color, then adding two neutrals, for example, would make a very pleasing three-color combination.

1. Accessory accents

Against the background of an emerald dress, neutral-toned accessories such as a belt, hosiery, earrings and scarf add a restrained, sophisticated touch. The other, more obvious way to achieve this effect is to wear a neutral outfit with bold, bright accessories.

2. Under-accent

Bring color out subtly but effectively by adding it under a neutral skirt and jacket combination. Here a pale yellow adds a blush of color. Vivid red would work as well, with a more dramatic effect.

3. Over-accent

The over-accent formula lets you enjoy wearing a color that is bolder than you usually choose. Notice the vivid red baseball jacket. Worn over the neutral black jeans and the charcoal-and-white striped shirt, this splash of color makes the entire combination come alive.

4. Half split

Here the choices are neutrals and pales but the half split works just as well using brights and pales. A pair of khaki pants topped with a pale pistachio "T" and sky-blue shirt, for example, is effective—as is a more vivid combination using red, black and grey.

1.　　　2.　　　3.　　　4.

Fabrics

The right fabric can make an ordinary piece of clothing extraordinary. A skirt that looks good on the hanger is of no use to you unless it wears beautifully all day long. When you begin to look at all the fabric choices available, you will find that there are more than you imagined. There are no rules about what you can and cannot wear. Cable knits, smooth knits, challis, twill... any fabric that pleases your eye can become part of your wardrobe. With the easy-to-care-for, durable, flattering choices available these days, you can wear fabrics as you never have before.

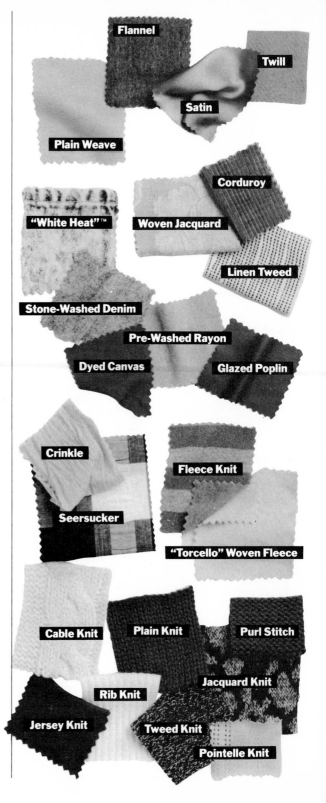

Flannel

Twill

Satin

Plain Weave

"White Heat"™

Corduroy

Woven Jacquard

Linen Tweed

Stone-Washed Denim

Pre-Washed Rayon

Dyed Canvas

Glazed Poplin

Crinkle

Fleece Knit

Seersucker

"Torcello" Woven Fleece

Cable Knit

Plain Knit

Purl Stitch

Jacquard Knit

Rib Knit

Jersey Knit

Tweed Knit

Pointelle Knit

The big news in fabrics is the refinement of man-made fibers. No more pooh-poohing polyesters. Now the finest American and European designers are creating fashions in all types of synthetics. These fabrics wear beautifully, require less care, drape perfectly and their colors are as rich and vivid as those you find in natural fibers.

Fabric glossary

We hear so many different fabric names. Jacquard, twill, fleece—what are they? What are stone-washed jeans? What is the difference between a knit and a weave? What are the choices in fabric finishes? "Pre-washing" is in—but what is it? The following fabric glossary is a quick way to unravel some fabric mysteries.

Natural fibers

These come from either plant or animal sources.
- Cotton. Made from a strong, absorbent plant fiber.
- Linen. Made from the flax plant. Linen is cool and absorbent.
- Wool. From sheep. A stretchable, soft, insulating fiber.
- Silk. Made by the silk worm. A strong, resilient fiber that is also insulating.
- Ramie. A crisp, cool fabric made from a plant fiber, similar to linen.

Man-made fibers

Many are produced from naturally occurring materials such as wood, coal and petroleum that are chemically altered to make new fibers.

- Polyester. A high-strength fiber that resists shrinking, stretching and wrinkling.
- Rayon. A cool and absorbent material known for its drapability, luster and ability to accept bright dyes.
- Acrylic. A soft, warm yarn that resists shrinking.
- Nylon. A strong, quick-drying fiber known for its stretch and washability.
- Spandex. An elastic yarn. Spandex is combined with other fibers to give clothes stretch and help them retain their shape.

Blends

Blends combine natural and man-made fibers to take advantage of the best qualities of each.
- Cotton blends. Cotton and polyester are combined for use in summer clothes because together they offer the coolness of cotton and the wrinkle resistance of polyester.
- Wool blends. Wool blends (usually polyester) offer the warmth and softness of wool and the durability and resistance to shrinking of man-made fibers.

Woven fabrics

All fibers can be used to produce either woven or knit fabrics. Woven fabrics are created on a loom.
- Plain-weave fabrics include simple poplin, challis, canvas and sheeting.
- Twill-weave fabrics, such as denim, herringbone and gabardine, have a distinct diagonal pattern to the weave.
- Satin-weave fabrics, such as satin-faced crepe, sateen and charmeuse, are flat, smooth and lustrous.
- Pile-weave fabrics have a deep-textured weave with a looped surface, such as terry cloth, or a sheared surface, such as corduroy and velveteen.
- Jacquard weaves, created on a special loom, are fabrics with patterned designs woven into them.

Knit fabrics

Knit fabrics are created from fibers on a knitting machine.
- Plain-knit fabrics, such as jerseys, are flat-surfaced knits.
- Purl-knit fabrics have a pebbled texture.
- Rib-knit and cable-stitched fabrics have deep-textured, vertical patterns in the knit.
- Pile-knit fabrics include looped knits, such as stretch terry cloth, and looped and sheared knits, such as velour. They can also be brushed, as in fleece.
- Jacquard-knit fabrics have intricate, multicolored designs.
- Pointelles are created by means of a variation of stitches that produce an open, lacy design.
- Marl and heather fabrics are two-toned or multicolored knits with a tweedy look.

Finishes

Many fabrics are treated or finished in various ways to alter their appearance.
- Pre-washing softens and preshrinks fabric, giving it a "not quite new" look.
- Stone-washing uses pumice stones, bleach and water to make fabric— usually denim—look broken-in.
- "White Heat"™ is Lane Bryant's name for a complex bleaching process that adds quick-years-in-the-sun to denim.
- Brushing gives a fuzzy finish to cotton flannel and fleece, creating an extra plush, soft feel.
- Glazing creates a shiny finish, flat and crisp, on cottons and blends.
- Heat treatments can add wrinkles, crinkles and puckers to fabric and are used in making textured fabrics such as seersucker, crinkle gauze and plissé.

Wearing stripes

The stripe is one of the most flexible and useful of all patterns. A widely spaced stripe against a white background is bold but not overwhelming. Multicolored stripes are very sporty; pinstripes are subtle. Stripes in combination—some vertical, some horizontal, of differing widths—are particularly interesting. On a shirt, stripes are crisp and clean; on pants and skirts, they can flatter the figure. Stripes provide a feeling of extra motion on a gathered skirt. Used as borders, they can add a delicate or daring touch. Whatever your Fashion Personality, you can use stripes to express your mood.

Tips

• A horizontal stripe on a top can be flattering if you wish to enhance your upper body to achieve a balanced proportion.
• A long, vertical-striped tunic sweater is slimming if you lack a well-defined waistline.
• Variations on stripes—zigzags or wavy lines—add a softer, less geometric feel.
• All striped garments should fit without pulling or distortion of the lines.

The shirt with narrow, vertical blue stripes and the horizontal-striped "T" with three buttons on the shoulder are two examples of the clean, sporty use of stripes for play or for work. The zigzag stripes give the skirt a dimensional look, while the sweater gets a fashion lift from striped borders. The stripes of the multicolored pants create the flattering illusion of a long, leaner line.

Checks and plaids

C hecks and plaids are very popular, and for good reason. They offer an endless variety of fashion looks. An oversized check top is great for a Bigshirt and can be easily coordinated with a basic outfit to bring in an accent of color.

Small checks offer a subtle introduction of pattern and color, while a pattern in houndstooth can be so small that it appears to be a tweed when seen at a distance.

Plaids in skirts and shirts are classic favorites. For a more current fashion look, tartan plaids and glen plaids are often used in suits and skirts.

Tips

● Large or small plaids can be flattering in skirts. The best choices are a small plaid in a pleated skirt, or a larger plaid cut on the bias so the pattern runs on the diagonal.
● Combining checks is fashion fun. Try to keep one much smaller than the other and make the colors subtle or matching.

The double grid of the shirt, above left, offers a fashionable variation on the classic grid. The pleated Madras plaid skirt is an exciting use of pattern, as is the oversized houndstooth sweater dress. The use of argyle on a sporty fleece is an oversized variation on a traditional pattern.

Bold prints

The options in big prints range from the all-over graffiti look to the single-image impact of the jacquard animal-design sweater in the illustration on the top right. As the phoenix emblem on the tweedy grey sweater dress above illustrates, bold graphics can be used on a wide variety of fabrics.

The use of graphically bold prints and single images or "pictures" can turn even the standard fleece sweatshirt into a fresh fashion. Bold graphics make an impact that draws the eye to the image, and they flatter the shape of any plus-sized woman. Terrific big prints are available in abstract patterns, letters, slogans and logos, florals and animal designs. Other possibilities include cartoons and maps. Anything you can print, you can print as a bold, wonderful top!

Tip

● When trying a bold print for the first time, select a casual, sporty top that you can wear often and you'll immediately get the feel for this style.

Small and medium prints

The small floral print of the skirt above, is a two-colored print in an all-over design that is so subtle it creates a swirling pattern. Another example of an all-over print, top left, is the witty South Seas print. The two sweaters show clearly how unique a small or medium print can be.

Small and medium prints can be very demure or as intricate and vivid as a Persian rug. These prints are appropriate in any season or situation and work well for dresses, tops and skirts. When used as a graphic design, they offer a modern, contemporary look. When delicate and floral, they are distinctly feminine. Small prints can also be used effectively as borders, in sections and in stripes on solid fabrics. In all varieties, the color combinations are infinite and can be used as terrific accents.

Tip

• When accessorizing a print outfit, select either the darkest or the lightest shade in the design for your accents.

Western

Mariner

Safari

Collegiate

The tried and true become fashion news

Fashion

Glamorous

Flirty

Ingenue

Dramatic

Female expressions come in many styles

Directions

Silhouette News

long

short

Fit-and-flare

With a pleasing symmetry and balance between broad shoulders and a full skirt, fit-and-flare flatters almost everyone. The key: a comfortable belt, wide or narrow.

Fit-and-flare, whether long or short, starts with an extended or padded shoulder. This silhouette is belted at the waist, and a simple full skirt completes the picture. Here an open V-neck adds a slimming vertical line. The short poufed skirt is a very contemporary example of one of the many varieties of looks this silhouette offers. Both flats and low-heeled pumps keep the proportions correct.

long

short

Long-over-flare

When you don't feel like wearing a belt, the long-over-flare is a relaxed silhouette that is stylish and feminine. The mood it creates is easy and comfortable on top and flirty and full on the bottom. This silhouette fits every figure effortlessly, for work, school or evenings.

Long-over-flare can be created with straight, lean tops, as the cardigan sweater on the left shows. When combined with a trim but full skirt, it is perfectly balanced. The short double-flounced skirt combined with the "T" is an example of one of the newest looks.

long

short

Long-over-lean

The most versatile silhouette, long-over-lean is the perennial favorite. One-piece dresses, skirts and sweaters, casual slacks and jackets are all adaptable to this silhouette.

Long-over-lean creates a streamlined column that gives height to the body. The "lean" bottom can be a straight knit or a slim pleated skirt. Kick pleats, slits and seams can help create the illusion of a lean line. Jeans and trousers are also the right choice for this silhouette. The long top can be straight or full and may be loosely belted at the hip or waist.

> **"** I was the third runner-up in the 1984 Miss America Contest. I starved myself for a long time to get to be the 'right' size. But when it was all over, I thought, 'This is ridiculous. What's wrong with me the way I am... naturally?'"
> —Wanda

Fashion Personality

Who you are and who you might be... just for fun!

Fashion Personalities are general categories that express a "look," a style, a particular flair that has a specific temperament. You may identify with one personality, or feel that you are a combination of several. You may even adopt a Fashion Personality just for a special occasion or event. We present the following Fashion Personalities to help you focus on the various looks that you can create through the clever combination of different Fashion Choices and Fashion Basics. We have illustrated each type at work, on weekends and in the evening to give you an idea of the possibilities that each Fashion Personality can explore.

Work: Bold prints, slim dress

Weekend: Denim and leather

Evening: Off the shoulder; knit and taffeta

- In a Word: Bold!
- Adjectives: Glamorous, sleek, chic, femme fatale
- Major Colors: All—particularly when worn head-to-toe
- Patterns and Prints: Big and bold, often abstract
- Fabrics: Leather, knits, sequins, denim
- Major Silhouettes: Long-over-lean, fit-and-flare
- Favorite Fashions: Accessories

Dramatic

"She walked into the room and every gaze was riveted on her."

Evenings: Angora and lace texture contrasts

Work: Soft dressing with a crisp touch

Weekend: Sporty skirts and well-detailed shirts

Romantic
"And she danced all night . . . ."

- **In a Word: Soft**
- **Adjectives: Näive, pretty, elegant**
- **Major Colors: Pales, mid-tones, neutrals in combinations**
- **Patterns and Prints: Small and medium, often floral**
- **Fabrics: Rayon, jersey, crepe, georgette, angora knits, lace**
- **Major Silhouettes: Fit-and-flare, long-over-flare**
- **Favorite Fashions: Skirts, dresses, blouses and sweaters**

Evening: The evening sweater set

Weekend: The striped polo and trousers

Work: Updated tailored look

● In a Word: Direct
● Adjectives: Tweedy, preppie, executive, elegant, clean-cut, traditional
● Major Colors: Neutrals, pales, deep tones in combination or head-to-toe
● Patterns and Prints: Small stripes, delicate prints, traditional plaids
● Fabrics: Twill, sheeting, knits, lambswool, denim, flannel, oxford
● Major Silhouette: Long-over-lean
● Favorite Fashions: Shirts, jackets, pants, sweaters, skirts

Classic
"Without effort she organized us all and solved the problem."

Work: Sweater dress and bold-patterned cardigan

Evening: A glittery, striped sweater with soft, cropped pants

Weekend: Classic shirt and fleece skirt

- **In a Word:** Eclectic
- **Adjectives:** Relaxed, comfortable, confident
- **Major Colors:** All colors in combinations
- **Patterns and Prints:** All
- **Fabrics:** All
- **Major Silhouettes:** All
- **Favorite Fashions:** All

Casual
"She does it her way... with spirit, humor and energy."

Shape and Style

Understanding your body shape is an essential part of awakening your fashion sense.

No matter what your shape, you can improve on Mother Nature by using a few tips on how to achieve the illusion of proportion. In the following pages, you'll see which styles work best for your body type. But no one is locked into any one set of rules. You can make different approaches work for you, sometimes with a few simple adjustments such as adding a belt or shoulder pads or trying a fuller skirt. Use the hints in this chapter to help you project your personality and enjoy trying new styles.

Whatever your shape, a tremendous range of fabrics and styles is available to you—including knits, the new, totally feminine fashion. Knits are replacing menswear in the office and on weekends, and the cardigan is taking the place of the blazer or jacket. Knits are flattering, comfortable and durable. Now is the time to add them to your wardrobe. A well-designed knit in a style appropriate for your body is a good choice for all shapes and sizes. You'll see that each shape in this chapter has an example of knit dressing.

More good news. Even if you've avoided them before, now you can enjoy tweeds, plush corduroy, cable knits and sleek high-shine fabrics. The key to flattering your shape is to wear clothes styled in cuts that accentuate your best features. Avoiding beautiful clothes is never the right choice.

The triangle is the most common body shape, with a trim top and wide hips. The waist is not well-defined, but can be easily given a shape with a belt. If this is your shape, you'll look great with padded shoulders and fashion's number one accessory, the belt. The fit-and-flare and long-over-flare silhouettes are great options for this body type. Shoulder pads balance the width of the hips, and the belt defines the waist.

• Wear prints or patterns in tops. Horizontal stripes are effective.
• Add definition to your waist with narrow belts, worn loosely at the waist or slightly below.
• Wear soft, flowing skirts, pleated pants.
• Use long, soft over-blouses, sweaters and shirts.
• Keep light and bright colors on top, darks on the bottom.

For play,
an oversized bold print fleece top that extends to mid-thigh and trim pants are well-balanced and create a flattering proportion.

For evening,
choose a flounced skirt and petticoat. Top it off with a soft, ruffled blouse, wide-shouldered and full.

For work,
a flared skirt and striped long cardigan sweater with strong shoulders, layered over a striped pullover is a dramatic option.

The Triangle

If you have a rectangular body shape—with shoulders, waist and hips the same width—you have a figure that can wear any fashion. All you must do to make the most of your Fashion Options is to create the gentle illusion of curves. You want to define your waist by wearing belts. Roundness and softness can be added with blouson tops and full skirts. You are able to wear any of the color combinations, silhouettes and all prints and patterns. Just remember to stick with soft fabrics and flowing lines.

● **Use a dark belt against a lighter-colored fabric to add more definition to your waist.**
● **A drop waist gives you a long line without sacrificing definition.**
● **Keep your neck line interesting, accenting its shape with bold jewelry or a ruffled, U-shaped collar.**

For play,
you can go for a gauzy, peasant blouse, a wide belt and cropped pants.

For work,
the softness of a jersey knit swing dress with a 2-inch mock crocodile belt can be complemented with sculpted jewelry.

For evening,
you might choose a pouf skirt with a drop waist and a simple torso with curved seams to create an elegant line.

The **R**ectangle

The **D**iamond

The diamond body shape has a trim top, wide waist and narrow legs and ankles. The simple tricks here are to call attention to your legs and to create balance with shoulder pads. You'll look good in dresses with a slightly dropped waist and in vertical stripes. The long-over-flare or long-over-lean silhouettes are very good choices. Wear prints and patterns below your waist or on a long shirt or cardigan: that directs attention away from your waist.

- **The new shorter skirts are made for you— take advantage of them.**
- **Shoulder pads are a must.**
- **When selecting a belt, a loose-fitting, narrow one is your best choice.**
- **A long cardigan sweater or jacket is a wardrobe basic.**
- **Wear low-heeled shoes to complement your silhouette.**

For play,
the vertical stripes on a long fleece top, with a turtleneck underneath, can be combined with rolled-up pants and flats.

For work,
a long, printed Bigshirt topping a dress with a slightly dropped waist gives the illusion of a defined waist.

For evening,
an open cardigan over a trim, long top and a narrow belt combined with a full print skirt creates an ideal long-over-flare silhouette.

With this rounded body shape, you should concentrate on creating a vertical line by using shoulder pads and long, lean tops. For accessories, long strands of beads are a good touch, emphasizing a long, vertical line. The long-over-lean silhouette works well if you choose head-to-toe color combinations. Prints and patterns should be worn either all-over or on the bottom only.

- **Create the illusion of a waist with thin, draped belts.**
- **To create a more angular appearance, depend on long tops with strong shoulders.**
- **Use color and pattern to create long, vertical lines.**

For evening,

a V-necked, softly draped top with a gentle yoke and shoulder accents combines beautifully with a two-tiered skirt. Long beads add to the illusion of a long, vertical line.

For play,

a long fleece top to mid-thigh with vertical ribbing is a good combination with trim jeans.

For work,

the two-piece knit with a lean skirt (don't be afraid of horizontal stripes here) and a long shirttailed polo sweater. Add a pin at the shoulder to direct attention upward.

The Circle

The **H**ourglass

The hourglass in any size is a wonderful figure, with its defined waist and balanced shoulder and hip measurements. You want to emphasize your waist. If you have ample curves, you may lessen them by using soft blouses and long sweaters to create a long, straight line from the shoulder to mid-thigh. Very full skirts are not your best choice—a knit or pleated skirt may be more flattering—but nothing is really out of the question for you. Consider the sexiness of soft cowl collars, gentle draped blouses and flounced skirts. Belts are your prime accessory, and the fit-and-flare is your natural silhouette. You can wear any color combination, print or pattern.

- **Wear lots of accessories: shawls, bangles, belts and necklaces.**
- **To emphasize your curves, choose soft, flowing fabrics.**
- **To make your curves less noticeable, try the long layered look.**

For play,
choose pull-on shorts and the basic "T."

For work,
an unconstructed long jacket and front-pleated skirt combined with a 10-button sweater and narrow belt makes a businesslike impression.

For evening,
dress up in glamorous style with a V-necked dress with a draped waist and soft skirt trimmed with ruffles. The all-over print is a great choice.

Lucky you! Your long legs look great swathed in full, swingy skirts—and with your great shoulders, there is no need for pads. You should concentrate on long vertical lines to minimize your bust. Draped blouses and asymmetrical cuts flatter your figure. Enjoy wearing belts, but keep them narrow—a half inch to one inch wide. You can wear all silhouettes. Colors can be combined using the half split or a dark under-accent. Wear prints and patterns below your waist.

- **Keep shoulders and torso soft and draped.**
- **Use the layered look with long shirts and jackets.**
- **Your best accessories are bracelets, belts and earrings.**

For evening,
a plunging V-neck narrows your torso and flatters your waist. Full skirts with bands of ruffles draw attention to your great legs.

For play,
a trim jean skirt topped with a black "T," a black belt and a long raglan-sleeved denim jacket is very contemporary.

For work,
an open V-necked blouse with raglan sleeves and a full plaid skirt with big pockets create a fashion look.

The V

Fashion Choices, Fashion Basics

Take a skirt, add the dash of a pullover, the ease of a cardigan and spice with accessories to taste. That's the recipe for a great fashion outfit.

But which skirt? What sweater—a sporty striped cardigan or a simple pullover? What are the choices, anyway?

Putting together a fashion wardrobe requires making decisions, and making decisions means you have to be familiar with your options. In this chapter, we will look at the Fashion Choices and Fashion Basics that are available, and give you all the principles you need to make the right wardrobe decisions.

Asserting your fashion sense is fun, and it's easy with the Lane Bryant mix-and-match system. We have designated each piece of clothing as either: ⓒ or ⓑ.

ⓒ Fashion Choices are the latest-breaking fashion news. Their patterns, prints and textures add surprise and excitement to your wardrobe. One fall you may find sweaters in many varieties of cardigans; the next spring pullovers may be the favorite. New styles may appear in skirts or jackets. Exotic patterns or prints may paint the stores in new hues. These are clothes that are fun and say "I am up-to-the-moment in fashion." A Fashion Choice is a new style and probably unlike anything else you have in your closet.

ⓑ Fashion Basics are versatile and enduring. They usually come in solid colors, and are designed to mix in combinations with your favorite clothes. From season to season they may appear in different colors or fabrics, with slightly different details. You will want two or three of each Fashion Basic in your closet to use as wardrobe building blocks.

Combining Fashion Choices and Fashion Basics

You convey your own personal style through your combinations of Fashion Choices and Fashion Basics. A Fashion Basic skirt in your favorite, one-color pleated style may not seem very expressive, but how you choose to combine it with Fashion Choices in sweaters or jackets can tell the world about your Fashion Personality. Moreover, one Fashion Basic skirt combined with a variety of tops can create many different fashion looks.

The essential categories of clothes that you rely on to build your fashion wardrobe are: dresses, sweaters, shirts, blouses, jackets, skirts, pants, shorts and T-shirts, fleece, swimwear and coats. They are complemented by essential wardrobe-building accessories: belts, jewelry, hair ornaments

Fashion Basic

This Fashion Basic is no Plain Jane—it is a one-size-fits-all sweater with fashion detailing: a polo collar and a placket front. As a good Fashion Basic, however, it is in a solid color and relies on traditional styling.

Buying Fashion Basics: At least two versions of this sweater, in solid colors, will work as building blocks for your wardrobe.

Mix and match: What goes with these basics? Almost anything, from jeans to skirts to pants.

Fashion Choice

This Fashion Choice sweater has a new, oversized argyle pattern. Notice that the bold pattern takes a Fashion Basic and makes it a Fashion Choice.

Buying Fashion Choices: Add Fashion Choices to your wardrobe in color combinations of old favorites or new fashion shades.

Mix and match: The argyle can top off any Fashion Basic pleated skirt in a dyed-to-match color—and it always adds excitement when worn with jeans or pants.

and hats, shoes and hosiery. In this chapter, we will look at each one of these items and explore the different styles of Fashion Choices and Fashion Basics that are available.

Headline news

Skirts: Even as hemlines go up, the graceful swirl of the longer skirt will not go out of style. And there will be other options as well: new flounce and circle styles, worn long or short, and lots and lots of lean and pleated skirts.

Dresses: The news is that knits are wonderful, wearable and suit every figure. Two-piece knit dressing makes it possible to mix and match, creating the illusion of many new dresses. The one-piece knit "accessory dresses," with their simple lines, are the perfect match for long cardigans or Bigshirts. They look wonderful with all styles of jewelry and belts.

Blouses: The latest style Fashion Choice features the addition of dramatically feminine shapes and details. News includes shoulder-baring styles, ruffled collars and U-necks.

Jackets: The news in jackets is really a sweater... the cardigan. It's longer and easier to wear over pullovers, blouses, shirts and dresses. The cardigan replaces the blazer and is worn for work and play with skirts, pants and dresses.

Pants: Reflecting the new styles, pants are softer and fuller. Many are cropped shorter.

This chapter is not a Lane Bryant catalogue. Some of the clothes that are illustrated are forecasts of things to come. Some are glimmers in our designers' imaginations. Others represent the clothes from the 1987 and 1988 Lane Bryant Venezia™ and JP® collections. Venezia™ is fashion that reflects the cutting edge of European-inspired contemporary sportswear. It offers women of all ages a selection of the most current silhouettes, colors, prints and patterns in shirts, sweatshirts, T-shirts, shorts, skirts, jeans, pants and dresses.

JP® is sportswear in the American tradition. It is the latest in classically inspired skirts, blouses, shirts, sweaters and jackets, and offers great weekend wear, coats, dresses and suits.

Now it's time to sit back, relax and enjoy planning your new wardrobe.

> " I have favorites—clothes that I wear over and over again with many different outfits. I make sure I wear them when I shop so that I can try on new clothes in combination with them. My favorite pieces of clothing are an extra-long cardigan, a full, swingy skirt and my bold-patterned sweater dresses."
> —Wanda

Dresses

Dresses, fashion essentials in any season, can be in classic or truly innovative new styles. Whether casual, go-to-work or elegant, they may be worn alone or topped with cardigans, Bigshirts or jackets. In any style, as the illustration demonstrates, they are a wonderful backdrop for accessories.

Dress silhouettes: The dress is a clean, efficient way to create a silhouette statement. Here the fit-and-flare dress has a belted waist; the softer variation is created with a slightly dropped waist and yoked hip line. The long-over-flare dress has a long torso, or dropped waist. The skirt can be flounced or full so that it creates a soft, draped flare. The long top may have a gentle blouson for softness. Long, trim lines here are shown in both knit and woven fabric. Subtle darts and gentle shaping help contour this lean silhouette.

Dress illusion: When is a dress not a dress? When it is a two-piece ensemble. A two-piece knit—sweater and matching skirt—creates the instant illusion of a dress.

Dress basics: The "accessory dress" is a wardrobe essential. Shown here are tank-top and cowl-neck versions. Their clean, simple lines are made for dressing up with many different accessories. Change the scarf, the necklace or the belt and you've got a whole new fashion. Both examples here are knits . . . again making exciting news.

One-step dressing plays many fashion tunes

Ariel Skelley

Fit-and-flare dresses with defined waists

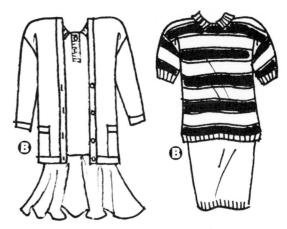

Two-piece dresses make the most of knit tops and skirts

Long-over-flare with blouson top and dropped waist plus a flounce of skirt

"Accessory dresses" are versatile Fashion Basics

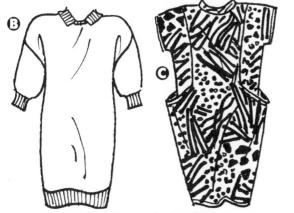

Long, trim lines in knit or woven

Sweaters

You can take them anywhere!

What's a sweater? An absolute necessity in many different situations. Every season brings new designs and new color combinations, so be on the lookout for what you love. On these pages, we've simply touched on the main Fashion Choices and Fashion Basics.

Sweater news

There are five categories of sweaters:

- *The tunic.* Worn long and out over skirts, jeans, pants and shorts, the tunic is comfortable and easy to wear.
- *The cardigan.* The big news now is that cardigans are taking the place of jackets at work and at play.
- *The pullover.* The mock turtleneck and the jewel-neck pullover are Fashion Basics that often come with matching cardigans. Pullovers are great tucked in or worn out.
- *The summer sweater.* Sleeveless or short-sleeved cotton knits offer texture and style as an alternative to blouses and shirts.
- *The blouse-sweater.* This new addition has details such as fluted collars, scarves or drapes.

Tunic sweaters

**The big news: cardigans; pullovers with
mock turtleneck and jewel necklines**

Summer sweaters in Fashion Choices

Fashion news in blouse-sweaters

Blouses

Classics, contemporaries and flights of fancy

Blouses have always been distinctly female. Today the blouse offers new details and is available in a range of styles that will suit any Fashion Personality. Among the innovations are sweetheart necklines, camisoles, draped collars and necklines with the added touch of scarves and ruffles. These newer looks join the classic blouse that is worn with jackets and cardigans, and blouses with off-the-shoulder flirtatiousness and loads of ruffles.

Blouse news

- For evening, the fancy blouse and skirt have become the latest in elegant dressing.
- Classic blouses have scarves, bows and ruffles.
- The camisole, the sweetheart neckline and the peasant blouse are very feminine and flattering.

Dramatic blouses for the evening

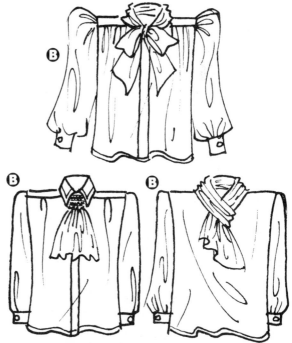

**Frankly female Fashion
Choices and Basics**

Detailing for Fashion Basics

63

Shirts

Taking the shirt off a man's back, women make it their own

Once women adopted the man's shirt, they turned it into one of the most interesting parts of their wardrobes. Available in cotton, cotton-polyester blends, rayon, silk, silky polyester; one color, plaid or striped, there is no limit to the shirt's variations. The fashion news is pockets . . . big and small.

Shirt news

Four types of shirts are center stage in fashion:
- *The Bigshirt* comes in bold prints, wonderful colors and every type of fabric. It can be appropriate for casual wear, work or evening.
- *Tucked-in shirts* are worn with pants and skirts for the clean-cut classic look.
- *The camp shirt,* a summer classic available in a rainbow of colors and an assortment of patterns, is made to be worn over T-shirts or tucked into a skirt.
- *Silky shirts* with open necks top off pants or skirts.

Leslie Priggen

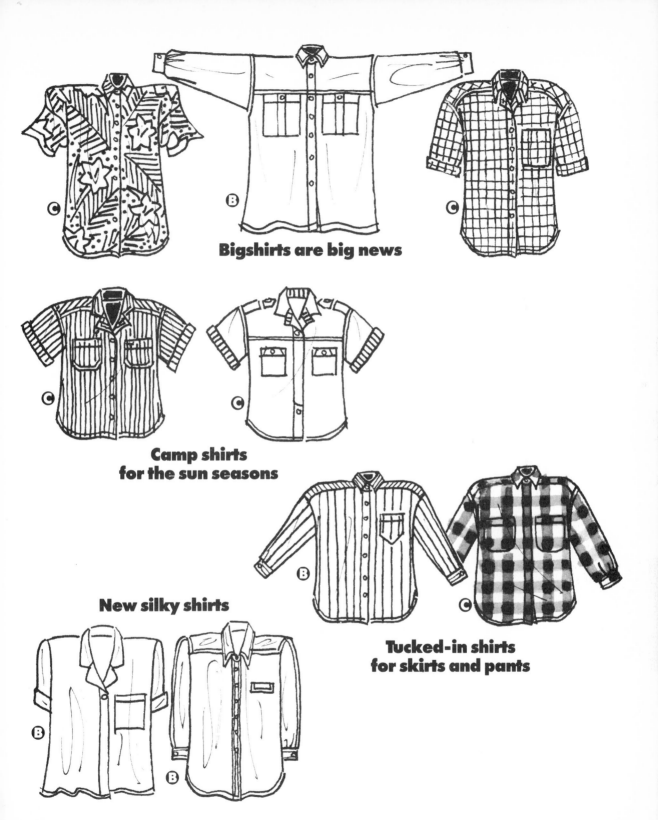

Bigshirts are big news

**Camp shirts
for the sun seasons**

New silky shirts

**Tucked-in shirts
for skirts and pants**

Cardiga

Jackets

Jackets take on the softness of sweaters

Blazers were a necessity for fashion wardrobes throughout the '70s and early '80s. But now, with the reemergence of the more feminine, Chanel-inspired, collarless cardigan look, women are choosing jackets that don't compete with menswear. We have the confidence to claim a style of our own! The blazer still has its place over long pleated skirts or classic dresses, but the new style is to wear the longer cardigans over accessory dresses and new fuller pants. The cardigan is earning its reputation as the jacket of the '90s.

Soft Bigshirts are summer jackets

Jacket news

There are four important jacket styles these days:
- *The knit cardigan* comes in standard or extra-long lengths with pockets.
- *Long, soft Bigshirts* are summer jackets and top everything for work or play. Look for them in a variety of prints and fabrics.
- *The jean jacket* in a bevy of styles makes this traditional American classic a new Fashion Choice.
- *The traditional blazer* now comes with a softer shawl collar.

Blazers hold t

are news

The jean jacket moves into the mainstream

ne for tradition

ALAN KAPLAN

67

Skirts

Pouf! it's a skirt; swish, it's a flirt; all together it's a new world of styles

Suddenly it's skirts, skirts, skirts, in pleats, flares, flounces and poufs. These are wardrobe builders—top them off in a thousand different ways to create all kinds of silhouettes and express different Fashion Personalities.

Here we have the four shapes of skirts: swing, lean, flounced and bubble. The soft swing skirts fall with a drape from an elastic waist or a yoke. Lean, straight skirts are in wovens or knits, pleated or plain. Ruffled skirts are layered in sexy flounces; bubble skirts are short for fun.

As for length, any skirt shown here could be long (29″ to 30″ from hem to waist) or short (22″ to 25″). You choose what you like.

Skirt news

- Details are back—pockets, buttons, pleats, kick pleats, gores and flares.
- Fabrics include rayon, cotton, lace, knits, challis, leather, denim, taffeta, fleece, flannel and wool.
- Hot prints are small and medium floral prints, geometrics and all-over abstracts.
- Silhouettes: Add long, lean tops to create long-over-lean or long-over-flare. Add belted tops for fit-and-flare.

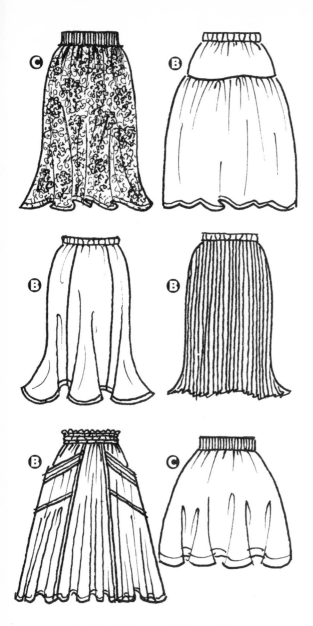

Soft skirts with swing

Lean skirts are perfect with long sweaters and shirts

The skirt news: Bubbles, ruffles, poufs and layers of flounces

Pants

Who's wearing the pants? The fashion-conscious woman

The menswear trouser is a classic fashion, but a new, more curvaceous line is here and it's making heads turn. In any season, pants are a fashion item that can be worn to flattering advantage.

Pants news

- Details include elastic waists, drawstrings, super pockets, zippers, seam-stitching and cuffs.
- Jeans are reborn in new fabrics including stone-washed, "White Heat,"™ and the iced look—pale pink, white and natural.
- New looks include a short, cropped leg from a gathered waist, or wide pajama legs.
- Classic trousers now offer more options. Choose cuffed/cuffless, slot pockets/side pockets, narrow waist/wide band, pleated/double pleated.

Ariel Skelley

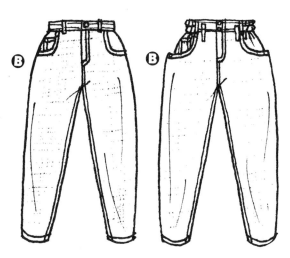

Jeans in new fabrics and colors

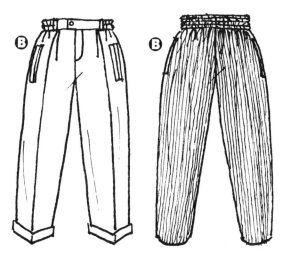

Trousers and pull-ons are classics

Crops

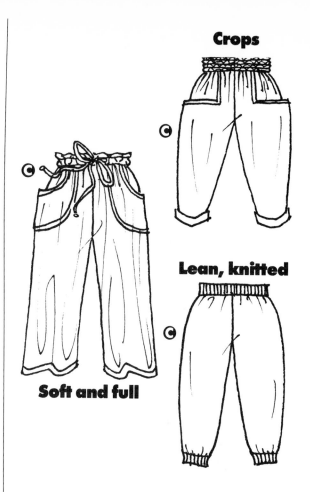

Soft and full

Lean, knitted

Rounded

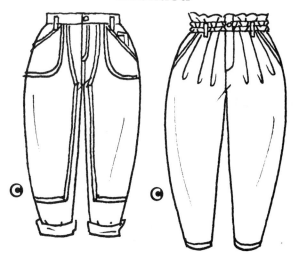

T-shirts and Shorts

Printed "T"s' graphics are fun

Runner's, tap and walking shorts suit "T"s to a tee

Pick a stack of "T"s for easy dressing; pack a stack of shorts for summer fun

The "T" is now a fashion mainstay that comes in an endless variety of styles. It is made for cool summer dressing as well as for layering under shirts and sweaters in spring and fall. You can wear a T-shirt with skirts, pants, jeans and shorts.

Shorts are very comfortable and easy to wear. The new shorts flatter all shapes and sizes and are particularly versatile when combined with "T"s and Bigshirts. Accessories such as the latest sports shoes and socks can give a shorts outfit an effortless fashion look, cool, crisp and self-confident.

T-shirt news

- *The feminine "T"* is the newest addition, offering the comfort of a "T" with the beauty of a blouse. Look for it in small prints and solid colors.
- *The tank* is an all-time favorite. Lane Bryant has tanks in dozens of great colors. Wear them under camp shirts or Bigshirts.
- *The button-front "T,"* worn in or out with skirts or pants, adds interest with detailing.
- *The classic polo* with long or short sleeves comes in a great range of fashion patterns and colors.
- *The crew-neck "T"* can be a Fashion Choice or a Fashion Basic, depending on its color, pattern and print.

Shorts news

Three styles of shorts are now making news: the runner's short; the full, flared tap short; and the classic walking short.

C

B

Feminine "T"s

B

B

B

B

**Fashion Basic "T"s:
The tank, button-front,
polo and crew-neck**

VENEZIA

Fleece

A secret cuddle—and a public declaration of casual style

Fleece is the material that makes your wonderful old sweatshirt so soft. And now it's the fabric that is used to create new Fashion Choices in skirts, pants and jackets. The newest fleece, Torcello, is a woven twill on the outside. It has been pre-laundered so it's extra comfortable.

Fleece news

• *Long fleece tops* make their mark now and will continue to do so in the seasons to come. They have lots of detailing—mock turtlenecks, zippers, quilting and appliqués. They can be styled as polo tops, crewnecks or tunics with bold prints and graphics for added interest.
• *Winter "T"s* are great warmers that can be worn under sweatshirts, sweaters and shirts to provide an extra layer of comfort. With double-rolled or turtlenecks and a Granddad buttoned front, they have the extra style that makes them terrific with skirts and pants.
• *The newest fleece styles* are soft, swingy skirts, modified jogging pants and shirts with knit trim.

"T"s for winter

74

Ariel Skelley

Long, lean fleece tops in great prints

Fleece sportswear in pants, tops and skirts

Swimwear

Revealing? You bet. Your swimsuit reveals your sense of style

Bathing suits are a sensitive issue for all women. It is especially difficult for plus-sized women to find flattering swimwear. Lane Bryant offers a full range of swimsuits, made to support, fit and flatter the fuller figure. In sizes 14 to 24, the maillot comes with soft support cups. Tunic and two-piece styles have more support and come in sizes 18 to 28. The most flattering creations from the finest names in swimwear design are available at Lane Bryant.

Swimwear news

- Bright colors and stretch fabrics are for you, and Lane Bryant has them!
- The maillot is a big favorite.
- Fashion ruffles and bold stripes make a flattering fashion statement.
- Diagonal stripes, and prints placed as accents on solid-colored swimsuits work well.
- Dark-colored bands at the thigh area make legs look longer.
- Geometric prints on blouson swimsuit tops are flattering to the round and diamond body shapes.
- Two-piece suits are the most comfortable style. Lane Bryant has a selection of tunic and blouson tops over separate bikini panties. With a side tie or drawstring they are Fashion Choices.
- These classic swimdresses are now updated with tropical prints and diagonal stripes.

Draped front with patterns

Ruffles and leg-lengthening color

Two-piece and tunic in stripes and prints

Coats and Outerwear

A coat is no longer just a cover-up. It's a wrap-up for a whole fashion look

The right coat will complement both your figure and your Fashion Personality. Look for a neutral color, the most versatile choice. Bright and pale colors add fashion excitement. Long coats may be dressy or sporty, narrow or flared, and—like all types of outerwear—are available in many colors and styles.

Coat news

• Current favorite choices are textured tweeds and quilted fabrics.
• Details—zippers, toggles, elastic waistbands, knit ribbed trim and hoods—are big news.
• Short coats and outerwear jackets are no longer confined to weekends or the football stadium; new styles make them appropriate anywhere.
• Raincoats range from the favorite trench coat to the newest high-shine plastic ciré fabrics.

Ariel Skelley

**New details on
classic stadium jackets**

**Long and three-quarter length
coats can be casual or dressy**

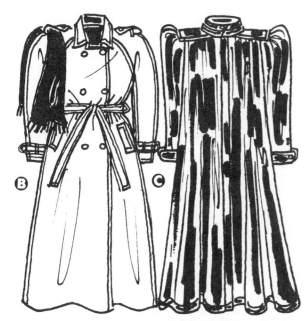

**Classic trench coat,
and fashion-shine raincoat**

**Short baseball
and stadium styles**

Accessories

Like icing on the cake or jewels in the crown, accessories are the finishing touch that can transform any outfit

Jewelry

Baubles, bangles and beads; necklaces, bracelets, earrings and pins have never been available in so many styles. From bejeweled to sleek, natural to high-tech, even humorous and outrageous, today's jewelry can change the character of any outfit instantly. Rely on it to double or triple your fashion looks.

At Lane Bryant, we have a complete line of all the latest jewelry in styles you'll love. Every piece in our collection is proportioned for the plus-sized woman. Our bangles are easier to slip over the hand; necklaces are longer for a graceful drape; earrings will suit your silhouette.

Jewelry news

- The wild and natural look—with wood, mock tortoiseshell, horn and faux ivory—is everywhere to wear with neutrals.
- Look for necklaces and earrings with primitive painted finishes.
- The antique look, with a patina finish and burnished metals, is in for all accessories.

Basic jewelry wardrobe

- One or two pieces of sterling silver or gold or semiprecious stones are wardrobe basics. A silver link necklace, coral earrings, a real cameo pin or a gold bangle bracelet are good starter pieces.
- Pearls are always in style and are wonderfully versatile. Textured or baroque pearls with an uneven surface come in a variety of sizes and are bold and contemporary. The classic pearl necklace is always in impeccable taste.
- Wear long strings of beads and layers of strands in various lengths. Mix beads with gold chains for the Chanel-inspired look. Wear rope-length necklaces with tunics or overblouses, but not with belted styles, which need shorter necklaces.
- Drop earrings are the number one fashion favorite.
- Button earrings, especially oversized, are an important part of your jewelry wardrobe.
- The big news in bracelets is the cuff: 2- to 3-inches wide in textured brass, gold or silver.

Tip

● Keep the scale of your jewelry accents in balance with the silhouette of your outfit—even when the jewelry is designed to make a dramatic statement.

Earrings

Hoops are an important Fashion Basic, most fashionable when they are big. Choose earrings that suit not only your face shape but also the length of your neck and size of your earlobe. Round faces are complemented by triangular or square hoops; heart-shaped faces look good with oval or round hoops; square faces are flattered by round shapes.

Pins

From flea market treasures to deco designs, antiques and bold sculpted shapes, even fantasy fakes loaded with lots of "jewels," pins add dash. Wear them high on the shoulder to draw the eye upwards. Nestle a pin on a lapel to make a traditional blazer come alive. Group three or more together for a daring touch—wear them for sports, work and evening.

Bracelets

Bracelets are wide, bold and bountiful. If narrow, wear four or five together. Watches, a recent favorite in accessories, are made to be changed according to your mood and your wardrobe. Wear your watch with chain bracelets or bangles.

Necklaces

Brilliant baubles for summer. Luminous pearls for that black dress. Strands and strands of chains and beads for day and evening. Sculpted bands, chokers and antique metal neck cuffs for drama on a turtleneck or against bare skin.

" Jewelry is not just for fancy dressing anymore. Wear it with fleece sports clothes for a touch of whimsy. Use it to brighten your look in any situation."—Wanda

Belts

The essential fashion accessory, the belt creates silhouettes and expresses your Fashion Personality. Lane Bryant has all the most exciting styles, and we make it easy to find belts that fit. Our sizing is based on dress sizes; for example, if you wear a size 18, your belt size will be 18/20. Sizes range from 14/16 to 26/28.

Belt news

The 2-inch belt boldly defines the waist and complements most skirts and dresses. The news is texture—mock animal skins such as lizard, ostrich and alligator. Buckles can be covered or gleam in sculpted silver, brass and gold tones.

The pant belt for jeans, trousers and pants comes in two popular widths: ¾-inch and 1¼-inch.

The hip belt, slung slightly low, often comes in soft shapes, with large sculpted buckles.

Contemporary belts

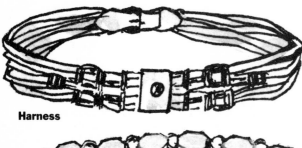

Harness

Concha

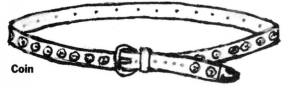

Coin

Pants belts

Stitched, webbed canvas

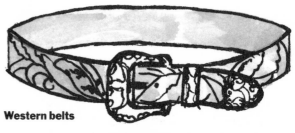

Western belts

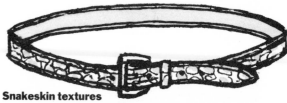

Snakeskin textures

Leather

Contemporary belts come in many unique shapes and designs. Some emerging favorites are the concha, the combination leather and metal and the studded belt.

The hip belt

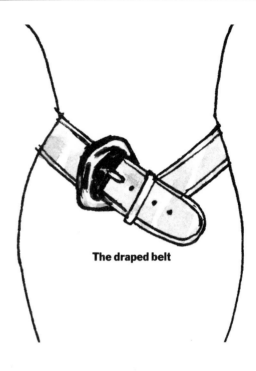

The draped belt

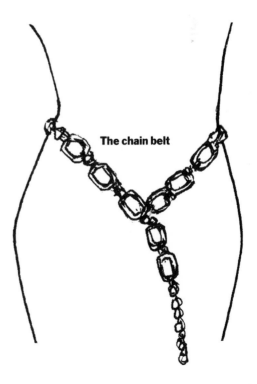

The chain belt

The 2-inch belt

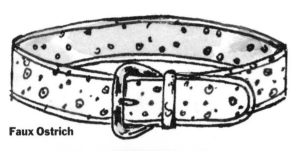

Faux Ostrich

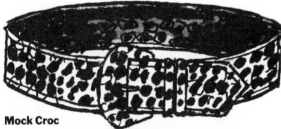

Mock Croc

Stretch

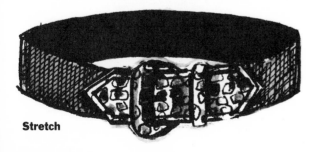

Stretch

Scarves

For drape, for shape, for accents of color and pattern, wear scarves at the neck, over the shoulder or tied in your hair for work, play and evening

Scarf news

- The old becomes new when you wrap a kerchief over your hair and around your neck. Add sunglasses, in the tradition of Grace Kelly and Audrey Hepburn.
- Long rectangles can be tied into bows at the neck.
- Thirty-six-inch squares in challis or heavy, silky fabrics can be worn knotted behind the neck for a cowl-like drape in front.
- Let a shawl-scarf in a paisley or wildlife print fall from one shoulder for warmth and color.
- Tie up your hair in a bright chiffon or sporty cotton bandanna.

Bows, berets and hats

Hot top news

- Today's wide-brimmed straw hat is wrapped with a pretty scarf for an accent of color.
- The baseball cap comes back in many fabrics and colors for all casual occasions.
- For day wear, the toque, the sailor and beret complete your working wardrobe.
- The latest barrettes come in mock tortoiseshell, dots and stripes, with jewels and glitter. Wear them two or three at a time.
- Try a tailored hair bow or a big pouf bow for evening or on ponytails, braids or a topknot. Wear it low at the nape of the neck for classic elegance.
- Hairbands—from mock tortoiseshell and patent leather to black velvet and satin—are for every occasion and can be worn with hair sleeked back or with bangs and curls.
- Flowers are back. Try them as a beautiful accent for fun or fancy dressing. Wear one over your ear or in the band of a ponytail.

Shoes and Hosiery

Your outfit ends with the right choice of hosiery and shoes, and your fashion look is not complete until your legs and shoes are perfect

Shoes set you in motion and create the visual sense of how your entire outfit flows. Flats allow you a springy stride and ease of movement. Heels require a more controlled, delicate pace. Although at Lane Bryant we don't carry shoes, they are important partners for our hosiery, so let's take a look at the shoe scene.

Shoes news

• *Flats* are now appropriate for day, work and evening. Look for textures—snakeskin, lizard, alligator and crocodile—plus patent leathers and suedes.
• *The semi-flat*—³⁄₄- to 1³⁄₄-inch heel—is for easy walking with a slightly more polished profile. Low-heeled shoes look great with all silhouettes, so forget old myths and wear the shoe you feel good in.
• *Active sports shoes* are now out of the gym and into the streets. With all the great variations on the tennis shoe, you need never suffer from aching arches.
• *The true high heel* is now a matter of personal choice. It adds a special drama to both office and evening wear. The key is to be comfortable in what you wear, walking and standing.

Socks

Socks are a major fashion accessory. They can be worn with flats and skirts as well as with pants, shorts and sports clothes. They come in many styles, from dainty anklets to oversized, sporty, slouch socks.

Sock news

• The Venezia™ slouch sock does just that—it slouches down around the ankle. Great with sneakers.
• The Venezia™ tweed sock has a classic haberdashery look when worn with pleated pants and oxford shoes.
• The Venezia™ triple-roll anklet is a versatile style that can be worn cuffed or not. It looks great with summer sandals, sneakers and all casual flats and sports shoes.

Hosiery

Lane Bryant has its own Lasting Comfort® pantyhose collection that is designed to fit plus-sized women perfectly, providing both comfort and fashion. Both hip and height measurements are used to assure you of comfort. Daysheers are made of all-purpose sheer nylon and are available with a reinforced toe or sandalfoot. They come in a range of neutrals and fashion colors. Silken Sheers contain spandex and have a special luster and a luxuriously smooth, silky feel.

● High heels: Pumps and straps for dress wear.

● Boots: Western, hiking and shoe boots for jeans, pants, trousers and denim or safari skirts.

● Sandals: Casual with shorts, skirts and dresses.

● Sports shoes: Classics revisited, from sneakers to deck shoes, for jeans and pants.

● Skimmers and low- heeled shoes complement any length skirt.

● Casual shoes: From loafers to espadrilles, great with all sportswear.

Intimate Apparel

Fashion is built upon the right foundation. But underwear is not just a practical part of getting dressed, it is also a private pleasure.

Lane Bryant knows how important well-made, beautiful undergarments are to the plus-sized woman. We have introduced a complete line of the most up-to-date styles of intimate apparel that flatter the figure and please the eye. Whether you are heading for the dance floor or the softball field, you can be confident from the inside out.

At Lane Bryant, bras and girdles are always of the best construction and reflect the finest fashion detailing. Panties are also available in a wonderful selection of colors, styles and sizes. And we have many special teddies, camisoles, slips and petticoats that will make you feel special at home or out on the town.

The complete intimate apparel wardrobe

A well-dressed woman has a wardrobe of foundations and lingerie for every occasion. Lane Bryant suggests:

For everyday or career wear
- 2 support bras that smooth and shape firmly.
- 1 underwire front-closing bra.
- 2 long-leg panty girdles for a smooth line under knits and narrow fashions (1 to wear, 1 to wash).
- 1 Body Briefer for an uninterrupted line of smoothness.
- 1 long-line bra for midriff control along with good bust support.
- 1 high-waist panty girdle for fashions that accent the waistline.

For casual wear
- 1 Lasting Comfort® Super Light bra, in pretty colors for fun.
- 1 Light Control Brief, for just a touch of shaping, color-matched to bra.
- 1 Triple Trimmer girdle to keep tummy under control; choose a brief, long-leg or pant-liner style.
- 1 T-back bra for "just enough" under "T"s and knit shirts, under anything sleeveless and casual wear.

Plus
- 1 strapless bra for bare sundresses and glamorous evening wear.
- 5 pairs of panties. Look for the flattering comfort of the Venezia™ high-cut nylon panties or cotton hipsters to wear under any loose-fitting clothes. Under pants and narrow knits, choose full-cut nylon briefs, since they won't show a panty line.
- 5 slips: 1 straight half-slip for narrow skirts; 1 flared half-slip for fuller skirts; 1 full-length slip for smoothness under narrow dresses; 1 taffeta slip for no-cling under knits; 1 lacy or frilly petticoat for fun under full skirts.
- 2 teddies: 1 to wear under skirts and suits, and 1 (frivolous) for sleeping.

Al Rubin

Tips

- Bras should fit without riding up. The most common mistake is to buy a bra that is too small in the cup or around the back.
- Measure your size each time you buy a bra or girdle to make sure your figure hasn't changed.
- Girdles should not be so tight that they bind. Buying one too small will create bulges at the waist and thighs.
- When you try on foundations, make sure you check the fit both sitting down and standing up.
- Panties with a cotton insert or all cotton fabric are cooler, and more sanitary and healthful.
- When wearing white outer clothing, there's less chance of "show through" if you wear beige or nude bras and panties.

Girdle glamour

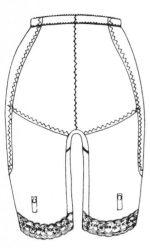

**All-Around
Maxi-Controller:**
For extra control and
comfort under all fashions.

The Body Briefer:
For a sleek, smooth line
under knits.

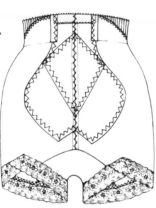

Trim-A-Waist Brief:
Smooths away inches
under fitted waists on
dresses and skirts. For fit-
and-flare silhouettes.

**Triple Trimmer
Pants Mate:**
Extra tummy support and
long, smooth silhouette
under pants.

Brief control

Super Light Brief:
Soft, flexible comfort
without binding, for line-
free dressing.

For a touch of ruffle
under full skirts
petticoats add fun.

Petticoats

The foundations and lingerie illustrated here are but
a part of the complete collection at Lane Bryant. For
those of you who want super-support or special
looks, we have everything from extra firm bras to
lightweight body liners (how about one in leopard
print!). Every garment is tailored to do its job
without binding. Come and visit our foundation de-
partments and talk with the sales staff to find just
what you want.

If the store you visit happens to be out of your
style or size, we can special order and have it for you
in two weeks.

Teddy topping

Comfort and sensual beauty at night with the frivolous sleep teddy.

The alluring day-teddy for the ultimate sexy fashion under all your best outfits.

Bra beauty

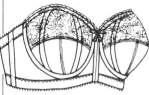

Dare to be Bare:
The strapless bra with extra-hold wide back, fits without binding for a line-free finish.

Leisure Ease:
A smooth cup with front closing for casual dressing and a sporty, natural feel.

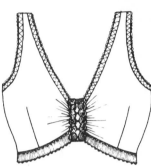

The Racy Bra:
The T-back gives support and comfort under T-shirts, deep-cut armholes and during active sports.

Front-Close Bra:
For smoothness, to wear under fine-gauge knits, silky crepes and any clingy, soft fabrics.

The Soft Touch Longline Shaper:
For a clean line under all clothes, it provides uplift and support plus trimming.

Lace Around:
Pretty and easy to wear with a front closing, this lacy bra separates and supports.

The Polishing Touch: Makeup and Hair

Makeup and hair are the all-important final touches to any fashion wardrobe. They assure you of a complete, well-coordinated look and let you put your best face forward.

As you will see in the make-overs, it doesn't take a lot of makeup to add glamour and beauty to your appearance. Makeup is not designed to cover up your face, but to bring out your own natural beauty. Selecting the right hairstyle is also an important way to accent your best features. So let's look at tips on applying makeup and selecting a flattering hairstyle.

Round: Use blusher to create stronger cheekbones by placing it in a sideways "V". Start under the center of your eye, extend color through temple and curve it up around the top of your eyebrow. Keep it subtle . . . for shading only. A touch of color on the chin will make your face seem longer.

Square: Apply blush on cheekbone, beginning below the center of your eye. Blend up toward temple. Use a touch of color on chin and forehead to soften the angles.

Rectangular: Place blusher on cheekbone below the outer edge of the eye. Extend upwards to temple to achieve the illusion of a wider, more defined face.

Heart-shaped: Use blusher to round cheeks, giving them definition and width. Start below the center of your eye, on top of your cheekbone. Place blush in semi-circle extending outward towards your ear. End blush below cheekbone.

Chin: To give definition to your chin and jaw, use a slightly darker blusher directly under the jaw. Smooth it down into an even tone.

Makeup

Applying makeup is a matter of creating accents and playing down certain features.

It's all done with light and shadow. To accent a feature, choose light, bright colors. To make it recede, choose darker tones. You should also use darker shades for contouring and for shaping your cheekbones and jawline. To achieve a natural glow, apply makeup over a light base of moisturizer, in the following order:
1. Foundation
2. Blusher
3. Loose powder
4. Eye makeup
5. Lipstick

Step one: Foundation

Foundation not only smooths skin tone, it can actually moisturize and protect the skin from the sun's harmful rays.
● Choose foundation to match your skin tone. Too dark, and it looks mask-like. Too light, and it becomes chalky.
● Change to slightly darker foundation as you tan.

Step two: Blusher

Blush brings a gentle glow to the face and is a wonderful way to accent face shapes or create contours. Use cream blush for dry skin and to give a touch of shine; use powder blush for normal-to-oily skin and for a matte finish.
● Blush should complement your skin tone.
● Ivory or rosy skin works best with true pinks, bluish pinks, rose and clear red.
● Black skin needs brick, magenta or wine-colored shades.
● Olive complexions look best in hot pink and plum tones.

- Beige or creamy skin is complemented by peach, coral or clear warm pink.
- Redheads should use terra cotta, light true reds and orangey corals.

Step three: Powder

A gentle dusting of translucent powder will help keep your makeup fresh and natural looking.
- Choose the same color as your foundation, or colorless translucent.
- Dust lightly over your entire face to "set" makeup. Then remove the excess with a soft powder brush.

Step four: Eyebrow Shaping

The eyes begin with the eyebrows, which too often are neglected. Today's fashion dictates a very natural look.
- Pluck brows gently, only on the bridge of the nose or under the brow to give a cleaner line. Do not over-pluck or make the brow pencil-line thin.
- If you have naturally thin brows, use an eyebrow brush to fluff up the hairs and apply eyebrow powder (one shade lighter than your hair color). Use eyebrow pencil to fill in, extending the line to a point that corresponds with the outer edge of the eye. *Never* use black pencil unless your brows are naturally jet black.

Step five: Eye makeup

Applying eye makeup involves using eye shadow, eye liner and mascara.
- Eye shadow should be used very subtly. Neutral shades are most fashionable and always look best for daytime. Choose colors that flatter your eye color and skin tone. The color of your outfit is not as important. Blue eyes are enhanced by deep greys, khaki and golden brown tones; green eyes seem brighter with violet shades and taupe or khaki; dark brown and black eyes light up with wine or plum tones. Dark eyes and dark skin look great with dark blue shadow.

- Eye liner is generally most flattering if it is dark grey or brown and applied in soft lines close to your upper and lower lashes. Only brunettes or women with raven black hair should wear black eye liner, and then only on the top lid, very close to the lashes.
- Mascara is a must for everyone. For fair-haired women, off-black or brown is best during the day. At night, black is flattering. Colored mascara is currently very popular for evening wear.

Step six: Lipstick

Lipstick is very important because it balances the effect of foundation, blusher and eye makeup. Natural tones, soft pinks, peach and clear light reds are good for most women during the day. In the evening, deepen the color.
- Lip pencils should always blend completely with the lipstick color you are wearing. Outline with them to keep lipstick from "bleeding," and to enlarge or reduce the shape of your lips.
- Lip gloss, applied evenly with a brush, is flattering to anyone. Use gloss alone for a natural look, over lipstick for special evening shine.
- Glittery or frosted lipsticks are for evening only.
- Very small lips look larger if you use medium-light or transparent shades.

Makeup tips

- For tired, red eyes, use blue eyeliner to make whites appear whiter.
- For puffy eyelids, use deep-toned eye shadow. Never use frosted or light shades.
- Don't mask puffiness under your eye with white cover-up; it will just accentuate the puffs. Use a deeper beige cover-up or foundation instead.
- Dust eyelashes with powder before applying mascara to give them a fuller look.
- For evening, touch up your basic makeup. Add black or dark blue eyeliner, a touch of deeper color to the crease of the eyelid and a touch of paler color as a highlight under the eyebrow.
- Use a bit more blush or a brighter color on cheeks for evening. (Night lighting fades out colors.)
- Use deeper or brighter lipstick at night. Add gloss on top of color for real glamour.
- Under fluorescent lights, avoid bluish-red or dark mauve-pink lipstick.

Hair

Clean, well-cut hair that flatters your face shape is essential for achieving a fashion look.

● Choose a haircut that is fuss-free. You don't want to have to spend hours on your hair, and it should keep its style even when you've been on the go.
● Evaluate your face shape. Your hairstyle should complement your natural contours.

A round face becomes more defined when the hair is layered and has some variation in line; keep the top full and layer the sides. Brush the side back at the temple and slightly forward onto the cheekbones. Avoid short crops. Use length to create an illusion of a longer face. Always keep the part to one side.

A heart-shaped face —with a wide brow and narrow chin—needs a longer hairstyle that has fullness at the bottom to balance the width of the face across the brow. Keep the top layered and trim, neither too flat or too high. A pageboy with the hair curled under below the ears is a good style here. Softly waved or curled long hair also adds width to the chin.

A square face needs height and softness to create a longer proportion and to lessen the regular angles of the face. Use styling gel to add lift to the sides and top of your hair. Use curls or fluffy bangs on the forehead to give added height and softness to your forehead. A square face needs hair that is either above the jawline or long enough to create the illusion of an elongated face.

A rectangular face benefits from width at the cheekbone and on the crown to balance the length of the face. Curly, wavy or long bangs combed to one side are flattering. Avoid long, straight hair; add fullness with a body wave or a permanent. A square cut bob—wide, with thick bangs—cut to just below the ear is a very good choice. Accent with big earrings for more width. Avoid long drop earrings.

> **"**Your hair can be your best asset. I have a very full head of hair and a square face, so I wear it full and flowing."
> — Wanda

Tips for the round face

● Add a dot of color to the chin for the illusion of length.
● Place a dot of light pink or yellow eye shadow on the center of the eyelid to "open" eyes and draw attention to them.

Tip for the heart-shaped face

● To add shaping and width across the cheekbones, place blusher in a V across the cheekbone and ending in the hollow of the cheek. Blend gently.

Tip for the square face

● To soften the angles of a square face wear your hair full and soft. Use blusher to create contours.

Tip for the rectangular face

● Keep the color above the center of the cheeks, always in a *curving* line, not angular.

Fashion Math™ Make-Over

What do all the fashion lessons add up to?

Fashion Math™!

It's the Lane Bryant system of wardrobe-building that proves once and for all that one plus one plus one can equal more than three. Your wardrobe dollar goes farther and the range of fashion options at your command is far, far greater than you may ever have imagined!

Fashion Math™ equals 2, 3, 4 or more outfits that can be rearranged in different combinations, creating many new looks.

Fashion Math™ uses Fashion Choices for a dash of excitement in your wardrobe. Your Fashion Choices are combined with your Fashion Basics, the building blocks of your wardrobe.

Fashion Math™ uses the combinations of colors and neutrals to guide you in the mix-and-match process.

Fashion Math™ can be used to achieve any silhouette and express any Fashion Personality.

Fashion Math™ formula

**4 tops
+ 3 bottoms
= 9 outfits**

Fashion Math™ lets you buy 7 pieces of clothing for $333.00 and combine them into 9 different outfits. That makes the cost of each outfit just $37.00!

Advanced Fashion Math™ formula

**4 tops
+ 3 bottoms
+ 4 duplicates
of Fashion Basics
in new colors
= 24 outfits**

The additional 4 duplicates cost $150.00—but you add 15 new mix-and-match outfits to your wardrobe! The cost per outfit is now a low $20.00. That's Fashion Math™ magic.

Shopping for Fashion Math™

When you go shopping for Fashion Math,™ you end up with a closet full of clothes that you love to wear. You can always return to the store to add more pieces because every season, Lane Bryant color coordinates all its separates. And every salesperson is well-versed in Fashion Math.™ Never again will you end up with a closet full of nothing to wear.

Twice-a-year Fashion Math™ wardrobe building

Spring and fall are the seasons that make you want to go out and restock your closet with the latest fashions and accessories. They are the perfect time to get your degree in smart shopping. On the following four pages, you are going to see complete Fashion Math™ wardrobes for fall and spring.

Fall Fashion Math™ adds up in knit dressing

Knit dressing is a way of life both for work and after hours. It offers elegant sophistication without sacrificing femininity. In addition, knits are exceptionally comfortable, wrinkle-free and flattering to any figure. The texture, style and silhouette of the new knits offer a choice to suit each body shape.

The fabric choices in knits are expanding, too. Pure wool knits are now joined by a whole family of blends and man-made fibers that retain their shape, drape beautifully and are available in every color imaginable.

For fall, be on the lookout for the long-line cardigan, the knit pleated skirt and the new mock turtleneck sweater.

Accessories are important because they provide both individuality and color. Especially new are belts in textures like lizard, ostrich and crocodile. Look for bracelets with sculpted shapes, and don't forget to experiment with scarves!

Spring into action

Spring brings a whole new world of Fashion Choices that focus on new colors and exciting silhouettes. The color headliners are neutrals in combinations with pales and prints, producing subtle accents.

Silhouette changes are shown in soft cotton skirts shaped with feminine flounces and ruffles, and the swing skirts. News is the knee-grazing shorter length.

Accessories are more whimsical in the spring: heart-shaped belt buckles, western belts and lots of decoration for hair, including bands, ribbons and bows.

Knit dressing

9 Fashion Math™ outfits made from . . .

2 Fashion Choices:
- cable cardigan in the new heather grey
- jacquard cardigan in a mix of colors

5 Fashion Basics:
- mock turtleneck sweater
- pleated knit skirt
- lean knit skirt
- knit accessory dress
- crew-neck tunic sweater

Total for Choices and Basics: $240.00.

Fashion Math™ Total: (including accessories) $320.00 for 9 outfits, or $36.00 per outfit.

+

Advanced Fashion Math™
Add 4 more Fashion Basics in new colors:
- mock turtleneck • pleated skirt • accessory dress
- tunic sweater

Total: $120.00.

Advanced Fashion Math™ Total: $440.00 for 24 outfits, or $19.00 per outfit.

+

Accessories
- 6 pairs of pantyhose • 2 belts: 1 faux ostrich, 1 hip belt
- 1 shawl scarf • 2 bead necklaces • 3 pairs of earrings
- 1 cuff bracelet • 1 chain bracelet **Total: $80.00.**

News in Neutrals
16* Fashion Math™ outfits made from . . .

4 Fashion Choices:
- bow motif sweater
- Madras plaid Bigshirt
- natural denim jeans by Venezia™
- short flounce skirt in soft cotton

4 Fashion Basics:
- swing skirt in rayon challis
- soft blouse in rayon challis
- cardigan sweater
- feminine T-shirt with crocheted edging

Total for Choices and Basics: $195.00.

Fashion Math™ Total: (including accessories) $270.00 for 16 outfits, or $17.00 per outfit.

we show 9, you find the other 7

Advanced Fashion Math™
Add 3 more Fashion Basics:
- swing skirt • feminine blouse
- feminine "T"

Total: $75.00.

Advanced Fashion Math™ Total: $345 for 34 outfits, plus accessories or $11.00 per outfit.

Accessories
- 6 pairs of pantyhose • 2 belts: 1 stretch, 1 mock croc • 5 bracelets • 1 large square scarf
- 3 pairs of earrings Total: $75.00.

105

Fashion Math™ Make-Overs

The lessons in this book can transform your sense of self, make you more beautiful and make you more confident. And they all add up to a glorious revival of your style. To demonstrate just how simple yet far-reaching the results can be, Olivia, Anita, Amanda and Susan are here for a Fashion Math™ Make-Over.

Olivia is a sophisticated urban woman with a love of fine things. She has enough energy to work hard all week and enjoy all that the city offers on weekends. She looks for easy-to-wear, simple clothing that is classic and well-styled. Her obvious strengths are her strong cheekbones, beautiful big eyes and perfect posture.

Anita, on the go all day at her job with a magazine group, has an effervescent warmth that reveals itself in the office and after hours. She is always involved in something—her hobbies are painting, fishing and relaxing at the beach. She has wonderful smooth skin and a radiantly natural beauty.

Amanda works in the quiet archives as a photo researcher, but her bold, dramatic personality comes through in all she does. Speeding to appointments on her bicycle, she is a streak of fashion. Her favorites are glittery sweaters for daytime and jewelry all the time—even at the beach.

Susan has just started her first job with a publishing company and the style at the office is casual, just perfect for her natural gentle style. On weekends, she's found with her feet off the ground—horseback riding, bicycling or Irish folk dancing.

Adding up to a new you

Each make-over includes the total Lane Bryant philosophy. We applied the information that has been presented in the book, step by step. This is Fashion Math™ in action.

Step one: Figure analysis

Look at your basic body shape to evaluate which silhouette would be most flattering. From there, begin to build a wardrobe. Olivia, for example, is a triangle, so we rely on shoulder pads and keep patterns and colors on top, with soft lines in skirts and pants.

Step two: Personality profile

The next step is to determine the Fashion Personality that best reflects your spirit and your desired self-presentation. For Amanda, we chose Dramatic dressing. It suits her dynamic style and creative work.

Step three: Lifestyle

Building a Fashion Math™ wardrobe that answers the demands of your day-to-day lifestyle is the key to achieving an active, wearable fashion look. The style at Susan's office is casual, just as Susan herself is in her off-hours. Anita's workplace is somewhat more sophisticated and style conscious, so her Fashion Math™ Make-Over blends clothing that reflects her love of outdoor sports with an extra touch of Fashion Choices.

Step four: Finishing touches

No make-over is complete without the most flattering hairstyle and makeup. The techniques used here are very simple and straightforward. There's no need to use a lot of makeup or complicated techniques to achieve a polished look. Chapter Five details these simple secrets.

> **"The Lane Bryant make-over can change your life and looks. Have a great time putting together all the facts from the book."**
> — Wanda

Selecting your Fashion Math™ wardrobe

When it comes time for you to shop at Lane Bryant for your new wardrobe, remember:
- Start with Fashion Choices and build the Fashion Basics around them.
- Build one wardrobe at a time. Don't try to combine clothes for evening with those for work or play. Sometimes they may overlap, but it is not realistic to expect to be able to cover all the bases with one Fashion Math™ equation.
- Let Lane Bryant's salespeople work with you. They are trained to assemble Fashion Math™ packages that suit any lifestyle.
- Don't put it off. The longer you wait, the longer it will be before you can enjoy the amazing transformation that the total Fashion Math™ Make-Over creates. Let Olivia, Anita, Amanda and Susan be your inspiration.

Olivia

“ It was quite an experience. I learned new ways to apply make-up. And the clothing is wonderful. I think it's great that Lane Bryant has more fashionable clothes for the plus-sized woman.”

Body Shape: Triangle
Fashion Personality: Classic
Clothing Choices: Simple sweaters, pleated skirts, trousers, blazers, swing skirts
Lifestyle: Busy career woman during the week; enjoys an active city life on weekends.
Fashion Math™
Wardrobe: For fall, we have chosen traditional office wear and clothing for weekends in the city.

Subtle use of eyeliner and shadow along the outside of the top lid accents Olivia's big, beautiful, almond-shaped eyes. Her cheekbones are given more definition with blusher and her lips are outlined.

24*
Fashion Math™ outfits made from...

Fashion Choices:
- cable-knit cardigan sweater
- striped shirt

Fashion Basics:
- flat-knit cardigan
- flat-knit button-placket pullover (makes a set with the cardigan)
- silky shirt
- pleated knit skirt
- flannel trousers
- shawl collared blazer
- swing skirt

Accessories:
- 6 pairs of pantyhose
- 2 belts
- 3 pairs of earrings
- 2 bracelets
- 1 pearl necklace

Total for Fashion Choices and Fashion Basics plus accessories: $380.00 for 24 Fashion Math™ outfits or $16.00 per outfit.

we show 9, you find the other 15

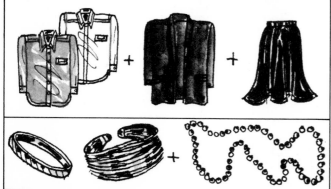

Advanced Fashion Math™
Add 3 more Fashion Basics from her original Fashion Math™ package in new colors:
- pleated knit skirt • silky shirt • flat-knit button-placket sweater Total: $120.00.

Advanced Fashion Math™ Total: $500.00 for 50 outfits, or $10.00 per outfit.

Anita

Body Shape: "V"
Fashion Personality: Casual
Clothing Choices: Flared skirts, jeans, sweatshirts
Lifestyle: Loves weekends in the country and outdoor recreation
Fashion Math™
Wardrobe: For fall and winter, we have chosen a casual wardrobe with a touch of sophistication for work and a casual wardrobe for weekends

Anita's beautiful skin and bright eyes are accented with warm pastel eye shadow, the use of subtle coverage under the eye and blush of color across the cheekbones. Rich, warm-toned lipstick makes the most of her smile.

22*
Fashion Math™ outfits made from...

Fashion Choices:
- print rayon challis skirt
- mock turtleneck fleece top with a zipper front
- "White Heat"™ five-pocket black jeans

Fashion Basics:
- one size polo-collar sweater by Venezia™
- one size crew-neck sweater by Venezia™
- cardigan sweater
- silky shirt
- straight knit skirt

Accessories:
- 6 pairs of pantyhose
- 2 pairs of earrings
- 3 pairs of socks
- 1 bolo necklace
- 2 necklaces
- 4 bracelets

Total for Fashion Choices and Fashion Basics plus accessories: $305.00 for 22 Fashion Math™ outfits or $14.00 per outfit.

* we show 9, you find the other 13

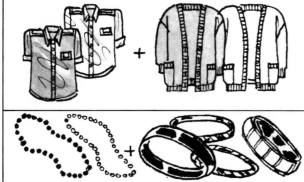

Advanced Fashion Math™
Add 3 Fashion Basics from her original Fashion Math™ package in new colors: ● rayon challis skirt ● cardigan sweater ● silky shirt
Total: $95.00.
Advanced Fashion Math™ Total: $400.00 for 44 outfits, or $9.00 per outfit.

115

Amanda

"Getting a new hair style, wardrobe and make-up really picked up my spirit. I like how the make-over made me feel."

Body Shape: Rectangle
Fashion Personality: Dramatic
Clothing Choices: Lots of glitter and jewelry
Fashion Math™ Wardrobe: For summer, we have chosen comfortable yet dramatic clothes for work and glittery fun outfits for weekends

Changing Amanda's hair style and using eyeliner to define her eyes gives shape and contour to her face. The touch of blusher and warm red lipstick bring color to her skin and make her glow.

15*
Fashion Math™ outfits made from...

Fashion Choices:
- tropical Bigshirt in rayon by Venezia™
- floral Bigshirt in cotton by Venezia™
- striped Bigshirt in cotton by Venezia™

Fashion Basics:
- tank dress by Venezia™
- swing skirt in rayon challis
- tank "T" by Venezia™
- button-placket "T" by Venezia™
- cotton sheeting pants with elastic waist

Accessories:
- 6 pairs of pantyhose
- 1 contemporary necklace
- 3 pairs of earrings
- 2 belts
- 5 bracelets
- 1 bandanna
- 1 flower hair ornament

Total for Fashion Choices and Fashion Basics plus accessories: $280.00 for 15 outfits, or $19.00 per outfit.

we show 9, you find the other 6

Advanced Fashion Math™
Add 5 more Fashion Basics from her original Fashion Math™ package in new colors:
- 2 tank dresses by Venezia™ • 2 tank "T"s by Venezia™
- swing rayon skirt Total: $110.00.

Advanced Fashion Math™ Total: $390.00 for 46 outfits, or $9.00 per outfit.

Susan

Body Shape: Hourglass
Fashion Personality: Casual
Lifestyle: Young career woman in a casual environment
Clothing Choices: Denims, corduroys and "T"s
Fashion Math™
Wardrobe: For all year round, we have chosen a casual wardrobe for work and sportier clothes for play

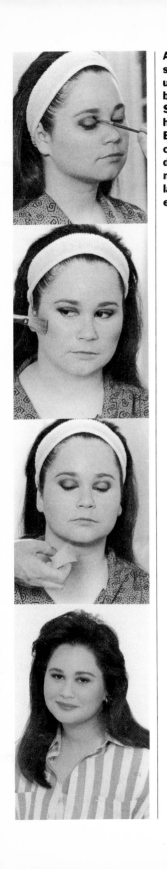

A simple change of hair style and the use of make-up to accent her natural beauty brought out Susan's beautiful eyes and her lovely, natural glow. Blusher under the cheekbone adds definition; eye shadow makes her eyes look larger and more expressive.

121

20*
Fashion Math™ outfits made from . . .

Fashion Choices:
- "White Heat"™ jeans
- wide-striped, pre-washed Bigshirt
- Venezia™ logo polo "T"

Fashion Basics:
- tank "T"
- button-placket "T"
- cotton pants with elastic waist
- pull-on corduroy pants
- cardigan sweater

Accessories:
- 3 pairs of Venezia™ socks
- 2 belts
- 1 bandanna
- 3 pairs of earrings
- 4 bracelets

Total for Fashion Choices and Fashion Basics plus accessories: $265.00 for 20 outfits, or $14.00 per outfit.

* we show 9, you find the other 11

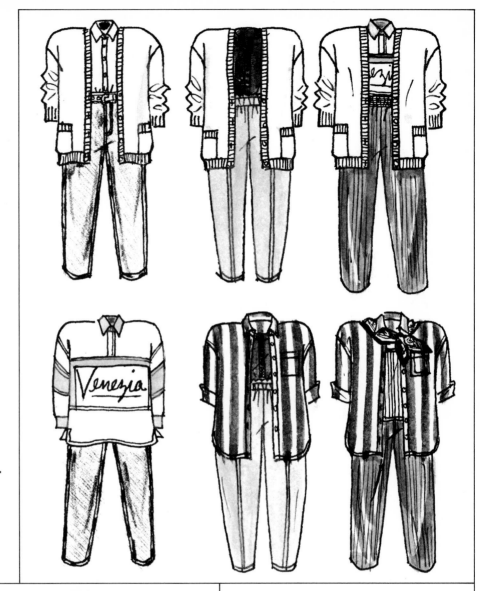

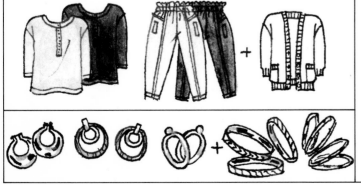

Advanced Fashion Math™
Add 3 Fashion Basics from her original Fashion Math™ package in new colors: • tank "T" • button-placket "T" • pull-on cotton pants Total: $71.00
Advanced Fashion Math™ Total: $336.00 for 42 outfits, or $8.00 per outfit.

Shopping

Shopping for clothes should be a pleasure—a chance to experiment, to use all your new fashion information and to see how you look in new styles and colors.

But very few of us were actually "born to shop." It is something that we learn by trial and error. Here are many easy-to-use techniques that will let you enjoy creating a fashion wardrobe. Don't deny yourself the opportunity of being your most attractive.

Lane Bryant's shopping system

Lane Bryant stores are designed to make shopping enjoyable. Everything—from the layout of the store to the dressing rooms, the sales associates and the clothes themselves—has one purpose: to make you feel great about yourself and confident about your ability to put together a wardrobe.

Sizing: The Lane Bryant sizing system is geared to help the plus-sized woman select clothes that will fit her perfectly.

Our measuring tape tells you your size—not your measurements—so that there is no guessing about what size skirt, blouse, dress or pants you should wear. There's no translating inches into sizes. No guessing about what size will fit you perfectly.

In addition, sizes are consistent throughout the collections. There is not one sizing system for dresses, another for skirts or blouses. It's easy to go from item to item, zeroing right in on those pieces of clothing that will look great on you.

Ask the sales staff to give you a size-reading *before* you start shopping—and you won't waste a minute looking at the wrong size clothes!

Color coordination: All Lane Bryant collections are dyed to match. Every season, we select the fashion colors that are making headlines. All our prints, patterns and solids are then dyed to work together in an endless combination of Fashion Math™ outfits. Putting together perfectly coordinated outfits is effortless—another Lane Bryant plus!

Sales help: The staff at Lane Bryant knows its Fashion Math,™ and is ready to help you assemble a complete season's Fashion Math™ wardrobe. No more wasted time or money; no more wondering if you'll ever find a top to go with that new skirt you bought.

These three basic parts of the Lane Bryant shopping experience are your assurance that you will truly enjoy shopping in our stores.

Make yourself look and feel pretty

Your single most important task when you go shopping for clothes is to start with a positive attitude. Compliment yourself. Don't worry over imagined flaws. And don't sabotage your chances of enjoying shopping by starting out feeling scruffy or not-pulled-together.

Tips for the reluctant shopper

In order to make the most of the Lane Bryant shopping system, you'll want to prepare yourself:

• Take time to get dressed up to go shopping. Wear your favorite, most flattering outfit.
• Wear underwear and foundations and hosiery that make you look and feel good.
• Make sure your hair and makeup are attractive and flattering.
• Wear shoes that will look good with the clothes you are going to try on.

Decide why you are going shopping

Did you ever go shopping, only to find that you wandered aimlessly from rack to rack, getting more and more frustrated every minute? Chances are you were suffering from the Wishy-Washy Shopping

> **"Shopping can be difficult when you are on the go and unsure of what to buy. When I started looking for attractive plus-sized fashions, I found it hard to get myself into a store. But then I discovered Lane Bryant... before they discovered me! Shopping has never been the same. It's fun to be able to buy clothes that make me look great... and to do it without breaking the bank!"**
> —Wanda

Syndrome. It's a common problem. Luckily, there's a cure:

• Decide before you leave the house if you are going to browse, not buy. That way you won't be disappointed if you come home empty-handed.

• Or, decide exactly what you are going to look for. Give yourself an assignment. When you get to the store, go directly to the department that has the item you need. Focus your attention. Then, after you've accomplished your task, look around and see what else you might like to buy. You'll feel satisfied that the shopping trip was time well spent.

• Rely on the salespeople. The Lane Bryant staff is eager and ready to help you. You don't have to go it alone! Salespeople are always there to show you what is available, make suggestions and give you advice about your selections. Let them help you use your shopping energy wisely so that you don't get worn out just trying to decide what to try on.

How to shop for a new wardrobe

Shopping for a new wardrobe is easier and more efficient than you may think. Just because you are going to put together seven pieces of clothing doesn't mean that it's seven times more work than shopping for one item at a time. (And in the long run, it's actually much more efficient because you don't end up with a closet full of clothes that don't match.)

Set aside time in your schedule for Fashion Math™ shopping. Don't try to squeeze it into twenty minutes between appointments.

• Browse for a while. If you are looking for two new skirts, take the time to see what is available. Look at all the styles, silhouettes, colors and prints. Don't try on anything right away.

• Reflect. Once you have surveyed the selection, ask yourself, "What did I like?" You'll be surprised. Two or three items will stick out in your mind. Those are the ones to try on first.

Adding it all up

Once you have experimented with all the suggestions we've given you, it's time to shop for a whole new Fashion Math™ wardrobe. This is where the fun begins!

- Determine the type of Fashion Math™ wardrobe you want: For work? For play? For casual weekends? For social occasions?
- Think about the Fashion Personality categories that appeal to you.
- Assess your shape (use Chapter Three as a guide).
- Select silhouettes that you like, that are flattering to your shape and that suit your Fashion Personality.
- Experiment with the various combinations of colors and neutrals in the patterns outlined in Chapter Two.
- Write out a short shopping list. Think about how many different outfits you would like to have for work, for example. Decide if you are looking for skirts and sweaters, dresses or a combination.
- Think about the accessories that you already have and make a list of those belts, necklaces, bracelets, earrings and scarves that you may need to round out your Fashion Math™ wardrobe.
- When you get to Lane Bryant to begin building your wardrobe, start by selecting the Fashion Choice items first. These unique tops, skirts, dresses or pants are the focus of your wardrobe.
- Choose Fashion Basics that complement the Fashion Choices.
- And remember, even though you are putting together a whole wardrobe, don't worry if you overlook a few items. The store will always have mix-and-match pieces that you can add to your wardrobe throughout the season.

In the fitting room

The fitting room... in other stores, it *can* give you fits! Even the bravest shopper can be intimidated. There is something about how we all perceive ourselves once the curtain is closed that can make this the most difficult part of shopping.

To conquer the fitting room blues, Lane Bryant has improved their fitting rooms so they are roomy and well-lit.

When you shop at Lane Bryant, remember the following tips and you'll find you can enjoy trying on your Fashion Math™ wardrobe:
- Take a complete outfit into the fitting room... don't try on one piece at a time. If you're shopping for a feminine, silky blouse, you'll never know how

Smile when you look in the mirror. It may seem silly, but it makes all the difference. If you're grumpy or dour, you can't be your most attractive.

flattering it is if you try it on with your blue jeans. Bring in a beautiful, flowing skirt so you can see how it will look as an entire outfit.
- When you get dressed, don't stare into the mirror. Turn your back to it until you have on the entire outfit. Then turn and smile.
- Step as far back from the mirror as possible to get a good picture of how the clothes work together and how they fit you.
- Move around, do a dance step, twirl or walk. Clothes (and people) are made to move!
- Ask the salespeople for their advice and feedback. They may have suggestions for changing the color of a top or trying another style skirt. Experiment, and let them cheer you on.

Savvy shopping

You deserve to look great and to enjoy making yourself your most attractive. There is nothing more satisfying than walking into your closet and knowing that you can get dressed easily, comfortably and with self-assured style.

So take the time to get familiar with your local Lane Bryant store. Come and visit us. We'll show you around and help you get acquainted with our collections. Feel free to ask lots of questions, and come back again and again. We want nothing more than to help you enjoy shopping so that you can walk out of the store with a whole new wardrobe that you will wear and love all season long.

Dear Friends:

Being the spokeswoman for Lane Bryant is an honor for me. But I also consider it a personal opportunity to do something that I believe in deeply: to communicate the Lane Bryant philosophy to women all over the country. It's my chance to let you know that you, too, can enjoy the pleasure of shopping for beautiful clothes and wearing the latest and most flattering fashions.

Lane Bryant has changed the world of plus-sized dressing for us. Thanks to Lane Bryant's fashion expertise and positive attitude to plus-sizes, we can all enjoy what every woman loves—wearing the clothes she's always dreamed of. Everything that's new in mainstream fashion is now available to all of us from Lane Bryant. And I say it's about time! Thanks a million, Lane Bryant!

I've been traveling across the country for Lane Bryant for a year now and have met many of you who are already enthusiastic customers. This book is my opportunity to welcome even more of you as friends.

In my tours of the country, I hope to meet lots of you personally. I'm looking forward to hearing what you think. Tell me what you like about our clothes and our stores—and what you'd like to see added or changed. If we don't hear from you, we'll never know!

Fashion Math™ Make-Over includes a lot of my ideas about dressing and shows you how to adapt these ideas for yourself using the Lane Bryant collections. But these are not hard-and-fast rules. They're just guidelines to help you create your own personal fashion look and express your own style—to look terrific and know it, to project an attitude of confidence and feel completely comfortable with yourself and your looks!

The plus-sized woman's time is right now. It's our time to look marvelous, feel great and have fun with fashion. Come on...let's put down the book and go shopping!

Love,

Vanda